Living With Less Neurons

Living With Less Neurons

*What's next after losing part of your mind:
A true story of life beyond stroke.*

By Jarvis Hooten

(Note to grammarians: Yes, the author realizes a more grammatically correct title would be "Living With *Fewer* Neurons," but that doesn't roll off the tongue or fit on a book cover as well.)

Proceeds from sale of this book shared with American Stroke Foundation.

Living With Less Neurons – What's next after losing part of your mind: A true story of life beyond stroke.
Written March 31 – July 12, 2020 By Jarvis Hooten
Edited By Tammy Parks and Jerry Hart
Cover Image: "Neurons" by Jonathan Cohen, NIH

Night Owl Ink Publishing
1661 Tonantzin Place
El Paso, TX 79911

NightOwlInk.com

Information in this book is intended for advisory purposes only.
Author is not and does not claim to be a medical professional.

ISBN, EBook: 978-1-7350426-2-6
ISBN, Paperback: 978-1-7350426-4-0
ISBN, Hardcover: 978-1-7350426-5-7
ISBN, AudioBook: 978-1-7350426-6-4

USA Copyright: 1-9424703191
Library Of Congress Catalog Number (LCCN):
2020919588

The secret to success and
happiness is overcoming failure
and misery.
−JH

Chapters

1 The Day My Life Changed

It started with a burning sensation in my right eyelid. I was sitting on the couch about an hour after dinner, and my right eyelid suddenly started stinging. Anyone who likes spicy food knows this mild pain. It happens when we absent-mindedly rub an eye after handling chile peppers. The acid from some peppers can stay on our fingertips for hours, even after thorough hand-washing. It's kind of amazing.

I'd had jalapeño slices with dinner, but they were from a jar. I had scooped them out with a spoon, not handled them directly. What could be causing my eyelid to burn like this?

Solving the mystery would have to wait. At the moment, the increasing pain in my eyelid called for action. I stood up from the couch and walked into the kitchen. Leaning over the sink, I cupped water into my right hand and splashed it on my closed eye. After a few splashes, the burning began to subside. I turned off the faucet and stood up.

Now I had a new problem – must have stood up too fast. I was so light-headed I had to place a hand on the kitchen counter to steady myself. My girlfriend, Colleene, noticed me from the living room and asked, "You okay?"

"I guess I stood up too fast," I said, puzzled because talking was suddenly difficult. My jaw felt as if it had been numbed for a dental procedure. What the heck was going on?

"What were you doing over there?" she asked, a little amused by my wet face.

"My eyelid was burning, like I had rubbed it after touching jalapeños." I was about to ask what she thought could have caused the mysterious burning eyelid, since I had not touched chile peppers that day. But my unsteadiness got the attention of Colleene's son, Brian, who was sitting at his computer desk in the living room. Brian rushed to the kitchen with a chair.

"You look like you need to sit down," he said. On another occasion, I might have thought he was overreacting. Not this time. I knew he was right. The wooziness in my head was making me feel very unsteady on my feet. I sat down heavily on the chair in the middle of the kitchen. The instability I felt was not what I would describe as dizziness. The room was not spinning, as if I had twirled around several times or just stepped off a carnival ride. The feeling was more a light-headedness – the stars-in-the-eyes sensation we get from standing up too fast.

Jarvis Hooten

After about five minutes of sitting in the kitchen, my head began to clear, but I still felt quite unsteady. Colleene suggested I should lie down for a while. On another occasion, I might have thought she was overreacting, too. I stood up too fast, that's all. On this occasion, something told me Colleene and Brian were both right. I needed to get off my feet until my head cleared.

I got up from the chair, slowly, and headed down the hall. Colleene was right behind me. She was concerned, but neither of us thought anything serious was happening. It was Friday evening, June 28, 2019. We were well into the summer heat of West Texas, so I was barefoot and wearing shorts. I didn't need to take off shoes or undress to lie down. Removing shoes and socks would have drawn attention to the weakness in my left arm. I could not avoid noticing my left arm felt limp as I lay down on the bed.

I was snoozing soundly within sixty seconds. Fifteen minutes later, I fully woke back up, feeling refreshed and revitalized. Wow, whatever that was, a little nap sure took care of it! The burning in my eyelid was gone, my left arm felt fine, and the fog in my head had completely cleared up.

Colleene happened to check on me at that moment. The mystery of the burning eyelid was perplexing. I was sure I had not touched any chile peppers. Had some chemical got on my hands while I was working in the garage earlier, and had I accidentally rubbed that chemical onto my eye?

A few minutes later, even as we discussed what could

have caused it, the burning in my right eyelid started again, worse. This time I was immediately light-headed, my left arm felt detached from my shoulder, and my speech was slurred and difficult. Trying to talk felt as if I had been tossing down shots of tequila since noon. It was difficult to speak clearly, and I could not stand up from the bed.

"Thith can'th be haffenning," I stammered. "Thefe are the thignsh of a thtroke."

Colleene's face went white. She got in front of me and told me to smile as big as I could. Unlike many stroke victims, my face had not gone slack on one side. She asked me to hold up my left arm and move it around.

Suddenly, instantly, my left arm felt normal again. I tried talking. "Testing, one, two, three. How's my speech?" I could speak normally again. My head was clear, eyelid had stopped burning, all in the blink of an eye. What the hell was happening?

I stood up from the bed and took a few tentative steps. Colleene, ever the worrying type, watched me intensely. I felt fine. I felt better than fine. I felt as if I had just woken up from a refreshing power nap.

We sat in the bedroom and chatted for a few minutes. Both of us knew I was showing indications of a stroke. Both of us also knew a stroke topped my list of scariest things that could happen to a person. One of my uncles spent the last third of his life in a wheelchair after suffering a stroke at age fifty.

Feeling better, and convinced I was okay, I was about to suggest we head back out to the living room to see what was on TV. Then it started again. The exact same sequence happened for the third time that evening: Right eyelid started burning, head became woozy, speech was garbled and difficult. My left arm felt as if parts of it were missing.

"Thish doeshn't make senth," I said, trying hard to enunciate each word.

"Okay, I'm calling 9-1-1," Colleene announced.

"But I don't have inthuranth," I stated flatly, telling her what she already knew was my one reason for not wanting medical attention. I'm not one of those men who won't go to a doctor when he should. It was not medical care that worried me; it was *paying* for medical care that terrified me.

I had been working a contract job as an RV Delivery Driver. Three weeks earlier, I had driven a luxury motorhome to Saint-Ambroise, Quebec, in northeastern Canada. It was a cool job for someone who loves road travel as much as I do, but it was contract labor. It did not come with insurance. I knew living without coverage at my age was dangerous. I intended to get insured as soon as I could afford it. This was no time to have a stroke.

I had driven back to El Paso from Canada to help Colleene and her family move into a new home. I was staying with them while waiting to renovate my house. This really was no time to have a stroke.

"You know what they say," she told me, sternly. "Symptoms of a stroke should be taken seriously and," she put extra emphasis on the next part, "should be treated *immediately*."

She was right, of course. I knew she was right. I also

knew I didn't want to spend the rest of my life paying off a huge medical debt.

"Please, let's give it a few minutes," I said, with perfect clarity. For the third time in thirty minutes, everything was normal again. "See there? It's going to be okay." How nice it felt to have control of my speech again. I waved my left arm around to prove to Colleene – and myself – that all was well. She had me smile again and inspected my face. I performed more test-talking and walking. When she felt sure my symptoms had passed, she conceded I didn't need to be rushed to a hospital.

It was after 9:00 PM. We decided to stay in the bedroom and watch some TV before turning in for the night. I had barely turned on the screen and started channel surfing when the eyelid burn came back.

"No, thish can'th be haffening," I murmured. Colleene was not waiting this time, and I did not try to stop her. She called 9-1-1.

It's a credit to El Paso's emergency response time that both an ambulance and a fire truck were at the house within three minutes. Suddenly, I was surrounded on the bed by five athletic young men – three firemen and two ambulance EMTs. The firemen stood by while the EMTs checked me over. The symptoms had passed again by the time they arrived. I was lucid, speaking clearly, and my left arm worked normally.

All my vitals checked out. My blood pressure was a little high at 135/85, but that was a typical reading for me. They asked me to smile big as they examined my face. They tested my right-handed grip, then checked that against my left-handed grip. They had me push up with my left arm as they pressed down on it, then did the same with my left leg. They checked reflexes, pupil dilation, range of motion, even tickled my foot.

Once they had determined I was not in emergency status, the fire crew decided to leave the scene. I thanked them and praised their professionalism. They wished me well, and the three headed out, leaving the two ambulance crewmen to continue examining me.

After some more testing, the head EMT – a very polite, professional fellow – explained what was happening.

"You've had a series of TIAs. That stands for transient ischemic attacks. Small blood clots formed in an artery to your brain, but they separated and allowed blood flow to resume. You have not had a stroke, but it is likely you will one in the next twenty-four hours. On the other hand, the clot may dissipate. You could take an aspirin to thin your blood now and another in the morning and be okay.

"The chance of the clot returning is high, though, so we believe we should take you to a hospital right now. We recommend you be monitored overnight. I understand your concern about insurance. As of now, our visit will not cost you anything. If we take you to a hospital, there will be an ambulance charge.

"If we don't take you to a hospital now," his tone was still friendly, but more serious, "will you assure us that you'll go to a hospital tomorrow morning and get checked out?"

I looked at Colleene. She turned to the EMT. He read her expression and said, "All his indicators are normal. If the TIAs start up again, you can call us right back." Then he turned to me.

"Forget about insurance. We," he gestured to his partner, "and everyone at a hospital want you to be healthy first. How to pay for it can be figured out later. Get to a hospital tomorrow, or call us back tonight if you need to."

Wish I had got this man's name. I'd give him a huge "Thank you" and "Job well done" right now. At least I had the wherewithal to tell him those things that night. He knew exactly how to handle my emergency.

It was almost 10:00 PM by then. I felt fine. Rushing to a hospital emergency room late at night seemed unnecessary. I promised the amenable EMT I would go to a hospital the next day. Colleene assured him she would call again that night if needed. I gushed gratitude and congratulations on their excellent jobs. They gathered their gear and were gone as quickly as they had arrived.

The ambulance team had spent about thirty minutes at the house. It was the most intense medical inspection I'd been through in years. Suddenly I felt very old and frail. No one had ever called 9-1-1 on my behalf. No ambulance team had ever examined me. The only time in my life I had been to an emergency room was at age eleven when I broke my arm playing football. My mom drove me to a hospital in our Volkswagen Beetle.

I had just learned what a TIA was, and that I'd had four of them in one evening. One of the life-changing medical events I was most afraid of could happen in the next twenty-four hours. It was terribly unsettling to learn that, not only could I be within hours of having a stroke, but that I *could* have a stroke at all. This was the kind of thing that happened to old, weak people. My fear of a stroke was about something that might happen years in the future. I was nowhere near as strong and healthy as I had believed when I woke up that morning.

The blue and red lights flashing onto the window curtains went dark. Moments later we heard the ambulance drive away. The house became quiet.

As I mentioned, I was staying with my girlfriend, Colleene, and her family. She has a son and daughter-in-law, and they have two young boys. We had all moved together into a four-bedroom, three-bath house on El Paso's west side. The house was perfectly laid out for such family living. One of the bedrooms, with an adjacent bathroom, was at the opposite end of the house from the other three bedrooms. It was just right for a "Grandma Room," separated from the rest of the family rooms. We called it the "East Wing" of her house.

The grandsons were a little nervous and upset from having an ambulance come to the house. I've known both boys since they were born, and we get along famously. Their mom had read to them in the master bedroom while the emergency crew examined me. Once the EMTs left, the boys came in to check on me. The little guys are not my blood relatives, but they were as comforting to me as I was to them at that moment.

Colleene and her daughter-in-law both worked jobs with early morning start times. Even though it was a Friday night, and the boys were out of school for the summer anyway, it was well past everyone's bedtime. We all retired to our various rooms.

Colleene and I settled down to watch some TV. We were both about ready to call it a night. I resigned to the fact that I was going to a hospital the next day. Knowing that was strangely comforting.

Damn it. Damn it to hell. My right eyelid started burning again. My left arm went weak, and I could hardly sit up from being so light-headed. All I could think to say, with great difficulty, was, "I'm sho shorry. It'sh haffening again."

Colleene shot out of bed. She grabbed her cell phone and was about to touch the screen when I said, "Wait. It's gone already." The signals of a TIA, which were disturbingly familiar by then, had come and gone in less than twenty seconds. Colleene hesitated, then put her phone down.

Fifteen minutes later, I had another one, my sixth TIA of the evening. This one was even shorter, maybe lasting ten seconds. Colleene insisted, and I agreed; if I had one more, she was calling the EMTs back. The sixth TIA turned out to be my last.

All the excitement must have exhausted us. We slept surprisingly well. Good thing, because the next day would be a doozy.

Jarvis Hooten

Stroke Symptoms? To The Head Of The Line!

Saturday morning, June 29, 2019: I got up around 9:00 AM. Colleene was up well ahead of me, as usual, and was in the living room sipping coffee. I poured myself a cup and sat down on the couch with her. I felt completely, utterly normal; no residual symptoms from the previous night's commotions.

Since the hospital was likely to do blood tests, we skipped breakfast that morning. I probably should not have even had coffee, but, come on, one cup can't hurt, can it? I felt confident my health was not in serious danger. I wouldn't back out of the trip to the hospital, but only because I'd promised Colleene. Besides, it couldn't hurt to be certain about my health status. A hospital visit would prove I was fine; I was sure of it. The episodes of the night before had simply been a wake-up call that I needed to work harder to lose weight and get more exercise. I had already started losing weight earlier that year and was quite proud to have shed about twenty pounds. The scare of the night before was motivation to keep me on my program.

We enjoyed a leisurely morning. I took a shower and put on fresh, clean clothes. None of us wants to be wearing dirty underwear when doctors and nurses examine us, right?

We headed for the hospital around 11:00 AM. I felt

altogether ordinary, like there was nothing in the world wrong with me, but Colleene wanted to drive. This meant she was really worried about me. She never wanted to drive, especially since she was still learning her way around El Paso.

Providence Hospital at Transmountain is a beautiful, fairly new facility less than three miles from the house. There was ample parking near the emergency room entrance. On that hot Saturday in June, I walked into the hospital entirely on my own power, fully upright and confident. I wasn't a young man anymore, granted. My knees sometimes gave me trouble, and I certainly couldn't run up several flights of stairs as I did in younger years, but I felt as strong and capable as most men my age might expect to be.

Nonetheless, the previous night's turmoil had provoked a profound, upsetting new awareness. I was dispirited to realize I had reached the age of fragility; I was old enough to start needing medical attention. Prescription medicines would soon clutter my dresser. How long did I have before sore hips and bowel movements became the things I talked about?

As we sat in the waiting room, a feeling of resignation overcame me. Whatever was about to happen was about to happen. I couldn't put it off for another decade, when I might think of myself as being old enough for a major health issue. I wouldn't wait until I could afford insurance. I would accept my fate and not resist whatever I was about to learn about my own mortality.

I didn't have to wait long. Seconds after signing in, my name was called. I was led to an examining room,

Jarvis Hooten

where a team of four or five specialists waited for me. Straight away, they had me on a gurney with my shirt off. A nurse attached heart monitors to my chest while another nurse took a blood sample. People asked me rapid-fire questions. When a person shows up at an emergency room with symptoms of a stroke, even if the symptoms happened the night before, that person gets top priority and fast attention.

Everyone on the emergency receiving team was impressively fit and young looking. They wore snug-fitting scrubs and athletic shoes. This group was designed to move fast without baggy clothes or clunky shoes to slow them down. They could have been a volleyball team as easily as an emergency room squad.

Soon I was being subjected to tests similar to what the EMTs had done the night before; someone pressed my left arm down as I pushed up, then vice-versa; someone held my arm up as I pushed down. They compared my right-handed grip to my left-handed grip. They tickled my feet and hammered my knees to test reflexes. I know of no other time when people looked at my smiling face so intently.

The whirlwind of activity lasted about ten minutes. Then everyone seemed to settle down for a moment. The head doctor, a youngish, handsome fellow straight out of central casting, gave me the rundown. He confirmed what the EMTs told me the night before: I'd had a series of transient ischemic attacks, which meant a highly elevated risk of a full stroke within twenty-four hours. My next step was to undergo a CAT scan, after which I would go to a hospital room for observation. There I would stay for the remainder of the weekend.

I looked at Colleene. She had expected this. I had not. I thought my visit to the hospital might last a few hours, not a few days. I thought I'd undergo some tests, be examined by a doctor or two, maybe have blood drawn. I'd be sent home with a prescription for a blood thinner and a stern warning to watch my diet and get more exercise.

I was about to suggest Colleene may as well head home, but she would hear none of that. She'd wait for me to come out of the CAT scan and go with me to the hospital room. Although I didn't like to feel I was putting her out, it was comforting to know she'd be there after the exam. This ordeal was beginning to feel a little scary.

Two nurses stood by my gurney as the doctor laid out the plan. Both were young, athletic-looking women. Those gals looked as if they could out-lift me in a gym and outlast me in a boxing ring.

As soon as the doctor finished outlining my schedule, one nurse said, "Okay, let's go," and they grabbed my gurney. A gurney is a hospital bed on wheels, but it was like riding a go-cart as those ladies propelled me through corridors to the imaging room. Remember, I still felt fine at this point. No stroke, no health worries at all. I was having a blast careening through hospital halls with those fast-footed nurses.

When we arrived at my destination, the nurses paused their frenetic pace long enough to introduce me to the CAT scan technician. I thanked them for the gurney thrill ride and for their impressive proficiency. They wished me well and were gone in a flash.

Ever had a CAT scan? If so, I don't have to tell you it is *w-e-i-r-d*. On that fateful Saturday in June of 2019, I was still blissfully ignorant to the many types of imaging used in modern medical technology. My experience never went beyond basic x-rays. I'd heard of CAT scans, of course, but I couldn't explain how that test differed from a cardiogram or an MRI. I had hoped to be twenty years older before I began experiencing those exams myself.

Thankfully, the technician prepared me for what would happen. It would be a cruel joke not to prepare a person, truthfully. A CAT scan uses a special chemical to highlight regions of the brain. This chemical is injected into the body through an IV port, which the speedy nurses had installed on me in the emergency room. The scan itself is painless and only lasts a few seconds.

The weird part is how a human body reacts to the special chemical. A few seconds after the liquid is injected, every person feels an unmistakable warming sensation in, of all places, their groin. You'd swear someone had poured warm water on your crotch, or, more commonly, people think they've peed their pants. This strange sensation doesn't happen in the feet, not in the back of the neck, not under the arms; it happens right in the nether region, and it happens to every person who undergoes a CAT scan.

When the test was over, I looked up at the technician and said, "That happened *exactly* as you said it would. Thank you for preparing me."

After the CAT scan, another staff person rolled me up to a hospital room. As I explained earlier, by this time I had resigned myself to the experience. When people get old, they start spending time in hospitals. It was time for me to accept I was getting old. I'd hoped it would be ten years or more before my first hospital stay. I still felt a little demoralized by facing my own frailty, but, if this had to happen, I may as well accept it.

The hospital room assigned to me was on the third floor. A big window filled one entire wall, allowing a pleasant view of the Franklin Mountains. The outside temperature was over a hundred degrees – normal for a summer day in West Texas. But the interior temperature was quite cool, almost chilly, which is common in hospitals. It was just the way I like it.

Colleene was waiting for me in the room. The orderly rolled me in on the emergency room gurney. I easily got up on my own power and walked the few steps from the gurney to the hospital bed. I had not yet had a stroke. I felt completely fine. Soon a nurse came in to start me on a saline IV. Apparently, it's common for potential stroke victims to become dehydrated. Another nurse came in with my first battery of medications. Everyone I encountered at Providence Transmountain Hospital was exceedingly polite and professional. I felt very well cared for, yet I continued to hope this was all unnecessary.

Each nurse jotted notes on a large chalkboard on one wall of the room. They noted what pills I took and at what time. Various attendants logged my blood pressure, temperature, and other measurements several times a day. Beyond keeping track of vital statistics, the hospital intended the chalkboard to be fun and personalized to each patient. Nurses asked about my favorite TV shows, sports teams, hobbies, things like that, and posted my answers on the board. One of the items was "Favorite Restaurant." People familiar with El Paso will get a kick to know my answer was Chico's Tacos.

By around 2:30, the commotion settled down. I had undergone all the tests and taken all the pills I needed for the moment. It was time to settle in and get used to my surroundings. I turned to my ever-supportive, always-reliable Colleene and confessed I was glad we were doing this. She was glad, too. No need for her to say it; it was written all over her face.

When I was all situated in the room, she left to pick up a few things for me from home. She would come back to hang out with me at dinner time.

Alone in the hospital room, I turned on the TV and started exploring my entertainment options. I did not want to think about the reality of my situation. Eighteen hours earlier, I had *almost* had a stroke – six times – and now I was planted in a hospital room for a whole weekend of observation. I got out of bed and sat in one of the armchairs to watch South Park, one of my favorite TV comedies. I hoped the familiar irreverent humor would inject some levity into my mood. It didn't. That favorite TV show let me down this time. It was difficult not to feel mopey. Even though all the tests I had been through showed me to be pretty healthy for a man my age, and even though I had not had an actual stroke, the *possibility* of a major health issue was now real to me.

One of my Granddad's favorite sayings was, "If you

live long enough, you get old." Most of us want to live long lives. We don't want to die young and miss out on years of interesting experiences, romantic adventures, and happy times with friends and family. We want to *live* well into old age, but we don't want to *be* old and decrepit. I did not like facing my first indicator of decline.

Colleene came back to the hospital room around 4:00 PM. I was so sure nothing serious was wrong with me that I asked her to bring my laptop. I intended to play computer games to occupy my time in the hospital. How absurd that seems to me now. We sat and chatted a while. I apologized for being so much trouble, just when we were getting her moved into a new house.

I called her attention to the chalkboard of my stats and personal information. We both noticed a disturbing line on the board. They had put down July 7 for my release date. What the ... that was over a week away! I was only supposed to be there a couple of days at the most for observation.

We asked the next nurse we saw about that far off release date. She assured us it was a tentative date. If I checked out okay over the weekend, I would not be required to stay that long. Nonetheless, I found it troubling that keeping me so long was even being considered. The TIAs of the night before had been scary, and this whole experience awakened me to the reality of my aging self, but I was going to be *fine*. All this fuss and hospital attention were unnecessary.

An orderly brought in dinner around 5:00 PM. It was pretty darn good, actually, and I was quite hungry by then.

Colleene stayed until 8:00 or so. I told her about the weirdness of the CAT scan. Like me, she had never been through that imaging test. Strangely, with all that had happened in the past twenty-four hours, we didn't find much to talk about. After I detailed the peculiarity of my CAT scan, we sat quietly, absorbed in our thoughts, as people who have known each other for years can do. She'd been with me most of the past day, so she knew everything that had happened. Neither of us had any idea what to expect would happen next. We didn't know what plans we could talk about. She would have stayed the whole night with me, if I had asked her to. But she hadn't had any dinner, and she's an early-to-bed person. I was beginning to feel tired from all the day's commotion, so I urged her to head home. She assured me she'd be back in the morning. Knowing her, I half expected she'd be back before I woke up.

The moment she left, I felt the loneliness of my hospital room. I had been road-traveling alone in Canada less than a month earlier. I'd slept in my car, by myself, at an ONRoute Travel Plaza in Ontario a few times. Being alone was not difficult for me. Being alone in a hospital room for the first time in my adult life, wondering if something might be seriously wrong with me, was unsettling. The loneliness passed after a few minutes. Everything was going to be fine, I told myself. I nestled in, watched some TV, and dozed off soundly within an hour.

Hospitals are not places for people who need rest. They wake patients up at all hours to check vitals and administer medications. Around midnight I was awakened from a very deep sleep for one of those routine disturbances.

The person who woke me was an angel in the form of a nurse named Priscilla. All the staff members at Providence Transmountain were terrific. Priscilla, however, was beyond terrific. She was a doll in nurse's scrubs. Priscilla could cheer up people after a plane crash. She was one of the sweetest, most charming people I've ever met. Even her name suggests a delightful character from a fairy tale.

Her reason for waking me up was to take my blood pressure and give me a shot. She also performed some of the familiar stroke tests I had done several times by then. In particular, she had me squeeze her fingers as hard as I could with each of my hands. She was a slender woman with pretty, girlish hands. I'm a big guy with what I'd like to think is an impressively strong grip. She took all the pressure I could apply without wincing. The grip of my left hand would become important within a few hours.

The syringe for the shot had a short needle, but it needed to be injected into the fatty tissue around my belly. Somehow, Priscilla made even that procedure not unpleasant. Thank you, Priscilla. The Providence Hospital staff is blessed to have you on the night shift, as are the patients who receive your care.

2 Was This Really Happening?

Priscilla woke me up two more times during that first night, at around 2:00 AM and 4:00 AM. I was a little grumpy from the abrupt, repeated interruptions to my slumber. Priscilla must contend with a lot of cantankerous drowsy folks on the night shift. Her cheerful demeanor was undaunted.

At 6:10 AM I was wakened again, this time by a wildly energetic male voice. Forgive me if this is politically incorrect. I do not imitate this man's accent to poke fun at him or Asian people. His manner of speech helps in understanding my bizarre first morning in the hospital.

"So, what go on heeyah? What wong with you, heh? You self-diagnose someting wong with you?"

I was sound asleep. It took a moment to remember where I was. Then it took another moment to lift my head, look for where this burst of questions had come from, and focus my eyes on the person making the inquiry. He was the stereotype of a man from southeast Asia: short, thin, built like a long-distance runner, with fine, jet black hair, and he radiated hyper-energy.

"I Doctor Rao. So, what wong with you? Find someting on internet and tink you got it?" The questions were sharp and accusatory. What had I done to upset this doctor? Do people commonly come to hospitals with imagined, self-diagnosed complaints? I had to wake up fast to respond to this grilling. Shaking away the clouds of slumber, I realized Dr. Rao was smiling. This was his way of kidding me!

"I assure you I did not diagnose myself," I began, mustering the energy to be deliberate. "EMTs came to my house last night and said I'd had some transient ischemic attacks. They insisted I should come to the hospital."

"Okay, now we getting somewheh," replied Dr. Rao. He looked me over and performed tests that were now familiar to me. He instructed me to smile big as he studied my face. With my left arm, I pushed upward against his arm, then downward as he offered resistance. It was the grip test that gave me *and* the doctor reason for concern. What the heck? I could not squeeze his fingers with my left hand nearly as hard as I had gripped Priscilla's fingers a few hours earlier.

After performing a very fast, frenetic examination of my left limbs, Dr. Rao gave rapid fire instructions to his assistant, told me he would check back later, then shot out of the room as quickly as he had come in. I lay back on the hospital bed, thinking I could get back to sleep.

Twenty minutes later, a nurse came in to check my vitals. Breakfast arrived twenty minutes after that. Hospitals are not for people who need rest.

Breakfast included a sealed container of yogurt. I had a devil of a time pulling off the seal. For some reason, I could not hold the container with my left hand. This was strange. Only way I could open the cup was to grip it in my right hand and remove the seal with my teeth. Was this a residual effect of my TIAs? No one had concluded I'd had a stroke – yet.

When Colleene came in, I told her about the dilemma of my left hand. My arm had not gone limp, as it had during the TIAs, but my fingers were difficult to control. Neither of us knew whether that was cause for concern.

Around mid-morning, a nurse brought pills and a cup of water. As I swallowed, I immediately felt the choking sensation when something "goes down the wrong pipe." I thought I had just tried to swallow the water too quickly, but the nurse took special notice of my coughing. Apparently, that was a bad sign. Strokes can cause people to lose control of their swallowing muscles, which, understandably, can be quite dangerous.

Lunch arrived around 11:30. Ordinarily, I was a big eater. I hadn't become overweight by not trying! The food at Providence Hospital was actually pretty good, but I wasn't in a frame of mind to eat much. I happily shared my lunch with Colleene.

Shortly after lunch, my dad arrived to pay me a visit. Although he'd been retired for years, he kept himself plenty busy. He was one of those old fellows who never seemed to have enough time for all his "projects." There were other things he would rather do than hang out in a hospital. I appreciated him taking the time to come see me.

Although I had spent all day in bed, my left arm and left leg still felt fine. It was only the fingers of my left hand that gave me trouble. I got out of bed and sat in one of the armchairs to visit with my dad while he was there.

Unfortunately, right then a staff person came in with a wheelchair to roll me to an x-ray room for a Barium Swallow test. The nurse from earlier had told Dr. Rao about my coughing after taking pills. As a precaution, he ordered the swallow test to make sure my throat muscles were functioning properly. I started to ask if it could be delayed until a little later in the day. The staff person assured me it was a short test, and technicians were waiting for me. My dad was understanding. He stayed and visited with Colleene while I got in the wheelchair and was rolled out of the room.

A Barium Swallow test was another new experience for me. Barium absorbs x-ray radiation (or doesn't absorb it – I forget which), so it stands out in an x-ray. This test is not a static x-ray image. It is a live video of the head and neck as a person swallows barium dissolved into various substances. Patients who take this test often want to watch the monitor along with the technicians. That certainly was the case with me. As soon as I understood this machine would observe my living skull in action, I wanted to see how that looked. It seemed most folks who take this test have the same desire. The technicians had a monitor set up where I could watch it.

They positioned my head against a brace, then turned

on the device. My skull appeared on the monitor, vivid as a computer-generated image. I received a cup of chalky white liquid, which I was to swallow as much as I could in one gulp. I took the cup and, watching the monitor, clearly saw my lower jaw tip down a bit as my mouth took in some of the liquid. It tasted as it looked – chalky and sweet.

The barium was white in the cup, solid black in the x-ray. How fascinating to watch my skull as the blob of liquid entered my mouth. I could see my tongue push the black cloud to the space behind my teeth. I tipped my head forward slightly, and swallowed. *Swish* – down my throat it went, right past my clearly visible spinal column. There was no "swish" sound, of course, but the video of liquid going down my throat was so clear, I thought there should have been.

Since the barium cocktail revealed no problems with my swallowing, we proceeded to the next item on the menu – an appetizer of barium gelatin. This was to step up the solidity of what I swallowed for the test. Gelatin was as easy to swallow as liquid, so thick, barium-infused crackers were the main course. I watched my jawbone and teeth crushing what looked like small rocks in the x-ray monitor. My molars pulverized the chunks into a black paste. Again, I could see the substance as my tongue pushed it to the back of my mouth. It held there for a moment, then – *gulp* – it propelled quickly down my throat, racing through the tube next to my spinal column. The barium-swallow machine was the coolest imaging device I'd ever seen. Wish all medical tests could be so fun and painless.

The entire exam took less than fifteen minutes, as the staff person had promised, and he rolled me back up to my room. This diversion had been downright amusing, but my enjoyment was short-lived. Right then, even as the orderly rolled me back to the hospital room, I noticed my left hand was becoming stiff, and a new pain had started in my left wrist.

My dad and Colleene were having a nice visit when I got back to the room. The orderly offered to help, but I had no trouble standing up from the wheelchair and transferring back to the easy chair. I told Colleene and my dad about watching my skull and spinal column on video for the barium test. As we chatted, I couldn't avoid the realization that I was having difficulty enunciating certain words, such as "Tylenol, particular, specifically," and "successful." My jaw and tongue felt heavy, as if I'd consumed a bottle of wine with lunch.

About an hour later, a nurse came in rolling what I surmised was a virtual presence device – a video monitor mounted on a pedestal over a computer. I was to have a virtual exam with a neurologist in California. My dad and Colleene stayed in the room. Dad sat by and watched with great interest. Like on a Skype call, I talked face-to-face with the neurologist. She had me perform the same tests I had done several times by then. I held a big smile as she closely looked over my face. I held up my arms, then lowered them slowly, and reached behind my back with one arm at a time. She asked lots of questions about my series of TIAs the night before.

The virtual exam lasted about fifteen minutes. The neurologist believed what I had begun to suspect – that I

Jarvis Hooten

had suffered a mild stroke, which explained my stiff fingers and difficulty talking. Beyond that, she could not offer a conclusive diagnosis.

The nurse rolled out the virtual presence monitor, and another nurse promptly came in to take my vitals again. (A person is not alone for long in a hospital room.) My indicators were a little high, but overall fairly good: Blood pressure was 130/82, heart rate and temperature normal.

I returned to the armchair and resumed visiting with my dad and Colleene. At that moment, I expected to be heading home within a couple of hours, or the next morning at the latest.

A pleasant looking blond woman, who appeared to be middle-aged but still slender and fit, entered the room and said she was my Occupational Therapist. Wow! I was already being assigned therapy? I expected to be out of there soon.

The woman's name was Jennifer. She had a soothing, pleasant demeanor. Jennifer examined my left arm, paying particular attention to my left hand. She was quite interested in what the neurologist had told me less than an hour earlier, so I summarized what the doctor had said. I was sitting comfortably in an armchair. I had on a pair of loose-fitting shorts and two hospital gowns – one to cover front and one for back. This hospital was thoughtful not to make patients leave their backsides exposed. Sitting casually with my legs crossed, my prevailing emotions were confidence and relief; I was confident my health was okay, relieved that I came to the hospital to get checked out. Discovering I had indeed suffered a mild stroke was distressing, but I fully intended to get myself in shape so it would never happen again. And I was satisfied this ordeal would be over soon.

After examining me, Jennifer seemed to reach the same conclusion. She had an engaging warmth in her face, with a hint of a twinkle in her eyes when she looked at a person. This woman lived to comfort others. Being a therapist was the perfect profession for her. "I don't expect we'll be seeing you much longer," she said with a pleasant smile, and she left me to continue visiting with my dad and Colleene.

It was after 3:00 PM by this time. Even with all the interruptions, I'd had ample time to visit with my dad, and he was fully up to speed on my condition. All of us were concerned that I'd endured a mild stroke, but relieved it had been caught in time, and convinced my hospital ordeal would be over soon.

When another staff person entered the room with a wheelchair and announced I was to have an MRI, there was a palpable moment of disquiet. Was an MRI necessary? This was yet another test I'd never had, but I'd certainly heard how traumatizing an MRI can be. My dad said, "Your mom had a couple of those, and she did not like them one bit." The MRI could take an hour or more. We'd visited plenty by then, so I suggested my dad should head on home. I started to ask Colleene to go home, too, but there was no way she would leave and not be waiting for me after the MRI. She did not function that way. Truth be told, it was comforting to know she would stay. This ordeal had just become scary again.

Medical tests had never disturbed me before. I was

Jarvis Hooten

not a person who avoided check-ups or shunned clinical tests. Medical exams are the tools for diagnosing illness. The only thing I'd heard about an MRI was the machine causes a person to feel claustrophobic. Having my head and upper body inside a big machine might be unpleasant, but I had never understood the huge dread over this test. I felt as much curiosity as apprehension as the attendant rolled me down to the MRI room.

~ ~ ~ ~

The MRI technician who greeted me had a cappuccino-colored complexion and wore a turban. As he shook my hand and greeted me, I could see clarity in his eyes and purposefulness in his movements – behaviors I associate with a person of intellect and learning. He had to wait for some kind of document before he could administer the exam, so we had time to chat.

Although the man's accent was subtle, he sounded clearly Indian to my ear, yet he was wearing a turban. I asked if he were a Muslim from India.

"I am from India, yes, but I am Sikh," he replied. I worried my assumption might have offended him, but his response was entirely affable. He seemed pleased, in fact, about my quizzical openness. I like learning about other cultures and religions. Admittedly, I was naive about Sikhism.

"I don't know as much about the Sikh faith as I'd like. If it isn't an impolite question, could you explain how Sikhism differs from Islam?"

My speculation that this was a man of intellect and learning proved true. He could have given a TED Talk on religions from Southeast Asia. Essentially, he explained,

Islam is a religion of submission; Sikh is a religion of devotion. In fact, the word Sikh derives from a Sanskrit word meaning "disciple," or "one who learns."

"Then you represent your faith well," I said. "Clearly, you are a person who learns."

The technician and I were the only two people on the entire floor, from what I could see. He said they usually didn't do MRIs on Sundays. The hospital had called him in from home for my test. Knowing this, I expressed dismay that I interrupted his weekend. His reply to that was priceless. "Ah, no, do not apologize. You have provided an opportunity for me to share my culture and make a little extra income this week."

A printer clicked on and hummed for a few seconds as it produced the document he had been waiting for. He had me sign the paper, and it was time to face the intimidating machine in the next room. My new Sikh friend rolled me through a door and helped me transfer from the wheelchair to a bench protruding from the giant, space-station-looking, doughnut-shaped machine. He handed me earplugs. This was unexpected. "The machine can be very loud," he explained. I would soon find out how true that was.

He instructed me to lie down on the bench face up and lower my head into a cradle at one end. Then he secured my head in place with two towels, jamming them firmly between my ears and the sides of the cradle. He explained the cloth was intended to keep my head immobilized and to further dampen the noise of the machine. I nodded, but the protections to my hearing perplexed me. MRIs are loud? This was something I hadn't known. He said the exam would last about forty-five minutes. Here was another thing I didn't know. I thought this would take five or ten minutes, like the CAT scan.

My thoughtful technician placed a cushion under my knees, which was very comforting. Lastly, he fitted a domed white grill tightly over my face, much like a baseball catcher's face mask. He peered between the slats of the mask and asked if I were okay. Barely able to hear him, and not able to talk or move my head at all at this point, I offered a wink and a thumbs up. I was ready.

I *thought* I was ready.

All was still for several minutes as the technician went into the control room. The only sounds were whirring air vents that seemed far away. Then it started; the bench began moving. My head and shoulders entered the big doughnut hole of the machine. A claustrophobic person would have a problem with this tight space, I could see, but, so far, it didn't seem at all terrifying to me.

There were a few more minutes of stillness. "This isn't so bad," I thought to myself. It would be frightening if I thought I couldn't get out, but the technician was right in the next room. If I really couldn't handle it, I could wiggle out of this thing, if I had to. I took in a long, deep breath, exhaled fully, relaxed my shoulders, and closed my eyes. The test would take longer than I expected, and lying perfectly still on my back would likely become uncomfortable, but, heck, this wasn't so bad.

A moment later, I discovered a betrayal. I had not been told the truth about MRI machines. It isn't claustrophobia that makes these tests traumatic; it's the noise, *noise*, **noise**! And these were not consistent, steady noises one would associate with a complex medical device. The MRI did not merely whir or buzz or drone loudly. It did make those noises, to be sure, plus a cacophony of other sounds that would have been comical, had they not been so loud and distressing. It was as if all the sound effects used by the Three Stooges were erupting in sequence at insanely high volume.

WHANG, WHANG, WHANG, WHANG, WHANG

... *pause* ...

burrrrreeeep, burrrrreeeep, burrrrreeeep

... *pause* ...

PEEdong, PEEdong, PEEdong

... *pause* ...

twik-twik-twik-twik ....

A kid with some sadistic noise-making toy could not come up with more outrageous clamor than that MRI machine generated. It was impossible to relax with so much hubbub, and the test seemed to go on for hours. The technician was graciously empathetic. Perhaps he'd been through an MRI himself, or he'd performed enough of them to understand what I was enduring. He came in the room every ten minutes to give me a time check.

"First part is done. Only about thirty minutes to go. You're doing fine." He patted my arm. Then, after what seemed like two hours inside a loudspeaker at a rap concert, "Ten more minutes done. You're halfway through. Now about twenty minutes to go."

When the exam was finally over; when I felt the bench begin to move, and my head emerged from the bowels of that infernal noise device, I felt a sublime release of tension mixed with a sense of accomplishment. I had done it. I had survived an MRI. It was an experience I now understood. I would have preferred to remain ignorant of this experience for another decade or more. That thought dogged me several times after my acquaintance with the friendly, erudite MRI technician. These procedures were not supposed to begin happening until I was *old*. I wasn't old yet.

The technician came into the MRI room and removed the mask from my face. I could have hugged him. He was my savior from the MRI monster, my bestest friend in the world at that moment. He helped me sit up. I started to remove the earplugs, then looked at him, tentatively. "Can I take out the earplugs now? Is it over?" That gave him a chuckle.

After forty-five minutes of lying flat on the hard, sterile bench of the MRI machine, a rigid wheelchair seemed welcoming and ever so comfortable. An orderly arrived within three minutes to roll me back to my room. Before we left, the MRI technician came over to me, shook my hand and held the handshake for a moment, "In case I don't see you again, it has been my pleasure getting to knowing you." [sic]

"I feel the same," I said, returning the sincerity of his gaze. "Thank you for your compassionate care and for the education about your culture."

The orderly rolled me down a few halls, up an elevator, and back to my room. He was friendly and cheerful, as were all the staff people I encountered at Providence Transmountain. As I rolled along in the wheelchair, I felt both elated and discouraged: Elated from being done with the MRI, discouraged because the weakness in my left hand was becoming worse, and it was moving up my arm. The consequence of my mild stroke was increasing, and it was spreading.

Colleene greeted me eagerly. The orderly helped me transfer from the wheelchair back to the armchair, which caused a new concern. This time I actually needed help getting from one chair to the other. A couple of hours earlier, I practically hopped out of the wheelchair, and now I needed help standing up. I attributed the weakness to being drained from the MRI. Except the weakness was decidedly more noticeable in my left side than my right, which meant I could not blame it entirely on the MRI. The test would have affected both sides of my body.

Something dreadful was happening, and it was becoming difficult to deny. The stroke's impact was worsening. More than that, my recognition of the stroke and submission to the stroke were taking effect, slowly and unalterably. My brain was suffering damage, and there was nothing I could do about it. A willingness to surrender took hold with disturbing quickness.

I related my experience with the astounding noise-generating MRI to Colleene. She noticed the difficulties I was having with my left hand and leg. Earlier in the day I had believed this ordeal would be over soon, that I'd be departing the hospital within a few hours. Now neither of us wanted to address how grim things were beginning to look.

Dinner was delivered at 5:00 PM. This time I was hungry. Colleene didn't get a bite of this meal. She stayed with me until around 7:00, then headed home to have dinner herself and get some rest.

My second night in the hospital was much the same as the first. One night of initiation to hospital survival had quickly accustomed me to being jolted awake every two hours. Priscilla was again the overnight nurse, and she was again delightfully charming.

Changing sleep positions that night, simply rolling over in bed, required more effort than normal. My left hand still had a fairly strong grip. I distinctly remember using my left hand to grasp the bed rail and pull myself onto my side a few times during the night. It was concerning that rolling onto my side required so much effort. I had to tug hard on the bedrail. This lack of mobility was about to become worse – the very next night I could not grip the bed rail at all with my left hand, and I certainly could not pull myself onto my side with my left arm.

My second morning in the hospital started as the first morning had – with a flurry of activity. Two doctors came in to have looks at me. Neither of them stayed longer than five minutes. I could hardly wake up enough to know what they did, anyway. A nurse came in to check my vitals, then another nurse gave me my morning battery of pills. By the time breakfast arrived at 7:00, my hospital room seemed like the lobby of a busy hotel.

Hospital food is usually thought to be bland and uninteresting. Not so at Providence Transmountain. El Paso's population is over ninety percent Hispanic, and my hospital food reflected the strong Mexican influence. Breakfast that morning was a kind of huevos rancheros ("ranch-style eggs") casserole. Having grown up in El Paso, I've had huevos rancheros plenty of times, but not in a casserole like this. It was quite tasty and quite spicy, which was fine by me.

Breakfast included a cup of apple juice in a sealed container. I could not open the container. The fingers of my left hand no longer worked. I couldn't even curl my fingers enough to touch my thumb, much less pinch and pull off the seal of a plastic cup. Packets of hot sauce also came with breakfast. Only way I could pry those open was with my teeth.

Colleene came in around 8:30. I had set my apple juice aside. When she came in I asked her to remove the seal for me. That was my way of revealing my hand didn't work. She looked at me knowingly. We still were not sure if I had suffered a full stroke, but, whatever had happened, it was becoming serious. I could no longer get out of bed without help.

We spent the morning watching TV and chatting idly. I had walked into the hospital on my own power less than forty-eight hours earlier. I had expected to spend no more than an afternoon there for tests. Now I could not stand up from the bed. My left hand was so stiff I could hardly move the fingers, and it was beginning to swell.

Lunch delivery was around 11:30. I don't remember what it was, but I do remember Colleene had to cut it up for me. I could not hold a utensil in my left hand. Colleene had not had breakfast that morning, as usual. She's not a breakfast person. After she assisted me to eat my lunch, I insisted she go get something for herself at the hospital cafeteria. She had to be hungry by then.

While Colleene was away, another doctor came in to see me. This was my first in-person visit from a neurologist. The only other neurologist I had encountered had been the one in California who examined me over a virtual presence device.

The in-person neurologist had reviewed the results from my MRI exam. She told me what I had started to expect. I'd suffered a stroke – a real, neuron-killing, paralyzing, life-altering stroke. I would need to stay in the hospital several more days.

The full impact of this news did not hit me right away. For one thing, I had begun to expect the worst had happened. For another, I didn't know yet what the worst that could happen would mean to my life. I was in analytical mode at that moment. I asked this neurologist what might have caused the stroke. I was relatively healthy overall. My blood pressure and cholesterol may have been a little high, but not at levels that would cause alarm.

"Well, you are obese, you know," she responded with unexpected condescension. Was that necessary? She just told me I'd had a stroke, and then she needed to be insulting? I knew I was over-weight, although I was not what most would consider "obese." The remark might not have been so annoying, had it come from a healthy, trim doctor. But this lady was easily twenty or thirty pounds *more* overweight than I was!

She also could not explain the burning sensation in my right eyelid that had occurred with all six of the transient ischemic attacks Friday evening. She suggested the burning eye was not related to the TIAs. That really frosted me. All six TIAs had started with a distinct burning pain in my right eyelid. Obviously, the burning eyelid was connected to the TIAs, yet she's trying to tell me they were unrelated.

My Granddad used to express mild disdain for doctors. "Doctors don't know what they're doing half the time," he used to say. As a kid, I couldn't believe he'd declare such a thing. My youthful belief was that doctors were above reproach, as were police officers and judges. I had learned by age eight that some teachers are not worthy of respect, but doctors and law enforcement were supposed to be infallible.

Granddad was right, I later learned. Some doctors don't deserve the adulation they get from society. Most are well-meaning, well-informed professionals, but some M.D.s really don't know what we expect them to know. We should listen to their council, but always follow up with our own research.

I don't believe police officers are all bullies, drunk with power over civilians, but there are a few bad apples in that profession, too. We learn these things as we age, and we learn how to accept them.

The unimpressive neurologist wanted me to make an appointment to see her again in a few weeks. The final insult came when I learned the appointment would cost me four hundred fifty dollars. Let that sink in. She charged four hundred fifty dollars for an office visit that might take twenty minutes of her time. That's an obscene over-charge, even if she were the best damned neurologist on the planet, which she clearly was not. I never saw her again.

Jarvis Hooten

Colleene came back from her lunch a few minutes later. I gave her the news. Like me, she had been expecting confirmation that I had, indeed, suffered a stroke. Soon we would have to begin planning how to handle this life-changing occurrence. On that Monday afternoon, July 1, 2019, all we could do was absorb the gravity of the situation. We didn't talk much that afternoon.

3 Reality Sets In – My Darkest Night

My fear of a stroke had been greater than my fear of a heart attack or even cancer. I'd seen what a stroke did to my Uncle Lloyd. His stroke was similar to mine; it paralyzed his left side and hampered his speech. He passed away at age seventy-five. That meant he spent a third of his life without the use of his left arm and leg. Now I had been struck by a stroke. How much would this change the rest of my life?

Neither Colleene nor I was prepared to discuss my future yet. She stayed with me the remainder of that Monday. I again needed her assistance to eat my food when dinner arrived. It was after 9:00 PM when she left – rather late for an early-to-bed person. She would have stayed later, if I'd asked her to. Thankfully, in spite of the overwhelming news of the day, I was becoming plenty tired and ready for sleep.

That night the full brunt of the stroke set in. My third night in the hospital was my introduction to the hell of stroke-induced spasms. I was just dozing off when the hamstring muscle of my left leg contracted violently, yanking my lower leg up with intense force. The shocking suddenness, pain, and ferocity of this contraction were similar to a charley horse, which I'd experienced in my calf muscles. I'd never had this kind of cramp in my hamstring. Like a charley horse, the spasm lasted a few agonizing seconds, then subsided. I could not possibly contract my hamstring with such force consciously. The exertion was so powerful, it made my knee hurt from having my lower leg crushed up under my upper leg. This was no fun at all.

Then it happened again a few minutes later. And again, and again, well into the night. Some of the spasms were two minutes apart; others were twenty minutes apart, but they kept happening for hours. Who knew torturous muscle cramps were associated with strokes? I thought a stroke resulted in *losing* sensation in body parts, not gaining unthinkable, painful contractions.

Imagine the worst charley horse you've ever had. Most people get them in their calf muscles. Sometimes it's a cramp that causes a foot to curl with painful force. Now imagine having a charley horse in the same muscle repeatedly every few minutes for several hours. That Monday night, after about the twentieth agonizing spasm, I began to doubt my sanity. But the spasms kept happening.

Because the contractions were so severe, as soon as each one was over, a strange thing would happen; I would feel remarkably relaxed. Sometimes I could go right back to sleep – unless the next contraction came along too quickly.

Other times I could not go right back to sleep, and those moments were when dark thoughts crept into my mind. Were excruciating muscle cramps my new normal? Was I going to be an invalid the rest of my life *and* suffer these painful spasms, too? There was so much more I wanted to do, so many adventures I wanted to go on, so many places I wanted to visit, so much more time I wanted to spend with loved ones.

Regardless of all I hoped to do, if all I had to look forward to was life as a cripple, I'd just as soon check out now. I'd been fortunate enough to travel more and try more things than many people get to do in a lifetime. Maybe I should be content with that. So what if I hadn't achieved a stellar career, become a millionaire, or been to another continent. I'd done lots of interesting things in my time. Some of my relatives and friends were rich and successful in their respectable careers. But how many of them could include "Game Show Host" on their resumes? How many had been to all forty-eight contiguous US states, plus much of Canada? Maybe that was enough for my time on Earth. I'd rather skip the rest of my life than live it out as an invalid, especially if agonizing cramps were to be part of my existence.

This dark thought came to me with disturbing ease. It was almost comforting to accept my life was over. This was the end, and I was okay with that. Turn out the lights, the party's over.

These were not suicidal thoughts. I did not begin calculating ways to do myself in. I simply felt comfortable with the possibility that, if I were to die then, I was ready to accept it. Living out a long life seemed an unacceptable prospect, if the rest of it was to be as an invalid with these torturous leg spasms.

The wretched spasms relented around 4:00 AM, allowing me to escape my gloom for a few hours of sublime sleep.

~ ~ ~ ~

Tuesday morning started with the same flurry of activity as my previous two mornings in the hospital. Nurses arrived to check my vitals and bring medications. Dr. Rao burst in with his frenetic energy. I told every medical professional who saw me that morning about the horrific cramps I'd had all night. To my amazement, no one seemed to know a damn thing about spasms after a stroke. Dr. Rao started me on a muscle relaxer, but he did not offer any solid medical advice. Were my cramps so unusual?

No, muscle cramps are not unusual after a stroke. I learned through later research that spasms and a condition called "spasticity" are quite common for victims of stroke. My Granddad was right again. Doctors don't know everything we expect them to know.

Breakfast was delivered around 7:00 AM. My left hand was now utterly useless. I did the same thing I had done the previous morning – ate what I could with my right hand and set aside items that needed two hands for

Colleene to manage for me. I didn't have to wait long. Colleene was there by 7:30. She had discovered a coffee service area down the hall from my room. She came in carrying two fresh cups of java.

She entered the room cheerful, but soon sensed my morose state of mind. I did not tell her how far I had gone into morbid thoughts the night before. I only described how the awareness of my condition was affecting my psyche. Even at best, I was about to face a long period of helplessness. Bless the woman; she assured me she'd see me through it, no matter what was to come. I also told her about the terrible night I'd had with leg spasms. Neither of us had any idea muscle cramps were associated with strokes.

We were not married, but Colleene and I had lived together for over a decade and had been through many trials and adventures together. We often joked that we didn't want to mess up our good relationship by getting married. Truly, I was blessed to have such a supportive person in my life. Colleene was every bit as committed to my well being as a spouse could have been. There was no need for an "in sickness and in health" contract. She had taken the entire week off from work to spend every day with me in the hospital, and she would figure out ways to look after me at home.

I tried to express how sorry I was that I was about to become a sizable burden to her, perhaps for a matter of years. She would hear none of it. Far as she was concerned, we could be TV-watching couch potatoes for the rest of our lives. Whatever was to come, we still had plenty more fun times ahead. Her kindness and loyalty did much to break apart my bleak mental state.

My dark thoughts were further diluted when Occupational Therapist Jennifer came in later that morning. Not to diminish Colleene's wonderful affection, but a professional therapist giving me good news really brought up my spirits. I expressed my concern to Jennifer about becoming an invalid, telling her what had happened to my Uncle Lloyd. She seemed genuinely surprised to hear I was having such thoughts. She'd seen people recover from far more serious strokes than mine. It would take effort, yes, and probably a year or more, and she could not guarantee the final outcome, but she was quite confident I would return to a normal life. She told me these things as she started my first ever occupational therapy session.

My left hand had swollen up considerably by that morning. There's another thing I never associated with stroke – painful swelling. Thankfully, after not finding anyone who could explain my terrible muscle cramps, Jennifer was well informed about stroke-related swelling. She massaged my left hand forcefully to encourage blood flow. I could not touch the tip of any finger to the tip of my thumb, but she encouraged me to try multiple times throughout the day. She assured me the brain finds new pathways to control muscles. I just needed to work at it and allow my brain time to re-route itself. Physical therapists, I would learn, are significantly more relevant to stroke recovery than doctors.

I received further lifts to my spirits later that day, not through therapy or other medical care, but through visits from relatives. Paul, my cousin once removed (he's the son of my first cousin, Jane – hope I got the terminology correct) appeared at the hospital, completely to my surprise. My dad had sent a group e-mail to the family to let everyone know I was in the hospital. A balloon bouquet arrived from my cousin in California, Sharon. Yet another cousin, Bill, and his wife, Pam, stopped in for a visit. Such an outpouring of concern encouraged my spirits.

That same afternoon, I had my first session with physical therapist Alex, another wonderful asset to the staff at Providence Transmountain Hospital. Alex was the first person I saw who knew anything about post-stroke spasms. Finally, someone who understood. He couldn't explain what caused them or offer an immediate remedy, but at least Alex was familiar with the terrible affliction. Here was more confirmation to my discovery that physical therapists are more important than doctors in stroke recovery.

The spasms had crushed my knee so many times during the night that it was badly swollen, and I could not straighten my leg without agonizing pain. Alex understood and did not demand me to do movements that caused pain. He helped me sit up in the bed and had me move my left leg as much as I could comfortably.

Then he tried some balance tests on me. He helped me stand up – a maneuver that demanded considerable exertion for both for us. I could only put a little weight on my left leg before lightning bolts of pain shot up from the injured knee. Only way I could stand up was by balancing on my right leg. That was okay, Alex explained. He could still do stability tests. He stood away from me a bit, so I was not leaning on him at all. Without warning, he shoved my left shoulder. He instructed me simply to sit down on the bed if my balance wavered. He gave me another, stronger shove; then several pushes from different directions. No problem. I could hold my balance quite well, if I judged his satisfaction correctly.

Alex offered the same, strong encouragement Jennifer had given; he felt certain I would recover and return to a full, capable life. He had worked with stroke victims who could not hold their balance against the slightest nudge, and I had managed to stay standing against some pretty hard shoves. That, he assured me, was significant in predicting a person's ability to recover from brain damage.

Alex and Jennifer are in the right professions. They are born caregivers. I felt better, mind and body, after therapy sessions with them. None of the doctors who saw me (and who later sent me astronomical bills) did anything nearly so beneficial as what therapists Jennifer and Alex did for me.

By dinner time, I'd been through another very busy day in the hospital. The previous day, Sunday, had been loaded with tests and examinations. Monday's activities marked the beginning of recovery in all levels – physical, mental, and emotional.

Colleene again assisted me with dinner. My left hand was almost completely immobile, and I had trouble even sitting up. Hospital beds are designed to assist people in such conditions. We raised the upper section of the bed, so I was sitting almost upright, and she spoon-fed me my supper. That's the first time I've needed someone to feed me since around age two.

Colleene left at 9:00 PM again. I settled in for my fourth night in the hospital. The spasms came back. Actually, the spasms hadn't stopped; during the day they occurred every hour or so. At night, when I was trying to sleep, the frequency increased to every few minutes. Sometimes I would just be getting over one spasm when the next one would hit. It was torture. The muscle itself hurt like hell from the repeated hyper-exertion, and the ferocious contractions repeatedly crushed my knee joint. Each spasm aggravated the sprain.

Now I understand what women go through during childbirth. Yeah, ladies, I know – men aren't allowed to claim we know what women go through during childbirth. So I did a little research on labor contractions. Uncontrollable hyper-contractions during labor are exactly what spasms are. Each spasm took over my entire body with its intensity. I had to struggle not to holler in anguish and wake up the entire floor of the hospital.

Out-of-whack neurons can flex a muscle beyond its capacity, causing savage, uncontrolled contractions. We cannot consciously contract a muscle beyond its normal limit. Flex any muscle as hard as you can. Really strain. Put everything you have into it. That's not the limit of your muscle's range. The brain can induce muscles to over-load themselves. This is what happens during childbirth contractions, and it's what happens during spasms. Will you moms allow that the severe muscle spasms I've described are at least kind of similar to labor pains?

Jarvis Hooten

By around 2:00 AM I was beginning to wonder how much of this I could take. After each spasm, my pain tolerance reached a new maximum. Sometimes there was a luxurious lull of thirty minutes between cramps. That's when I would sleep. Other times the breaks between spasms were only thirty seconds. Those occasions made me understand how a person could become addicted to pain pills or, when pills aren't enough, I realized how a person could welcome death. Anything to stop the agony was acceptable.

Wednesday morning was a bit calmer than my previous three mornings in the hospital. A nurse came in to check my vitals. Another nurse brought my morning battery of pills. When breakfast was delivered, I didn't even try to sit up and eat. I'd wait for Colleene. My mind was in a fog from lack of sleep, and my knee throbbed with pain.

Colleene immediately sensed my discomfort when she arrived. She asked what was wrong. I tried to explain the delirium of repeated spasms, how the contractions had apparently sprained my knee, and now the sprained knee hurt, a lot. She lifted up the covers to look at my knee. It was badly swollen. I had to keep my left leg slightly bent. Straightening it out caused shocks of pain.

She fed me the breakfast I had set aside. I was surprisingly hungry, and getting some food into my system seemed to make me feel better. Also, of course, some caring attention did much to soothe my pain.

Jennifer came in later that morning for an occupational therapy session. She did not like how much my left hand was swelling. I could hardly curl my fingers at all, so we didn't do any hand exercises. She thoroughly massaged the hand again to stimulate circulation. She also brought a thick nylon sleeve that slid tightly over my hand. The steady compression was intended to reduce swelling.

Minutes after Jennifer's visit, Alex came in for a physical therapy session. He brought along a walker and a sturdily built assistant named Louis. The walker had been fitted with an attachment on the left side – an extension from the hand grip with a cradle for my left forearm. This allowed me to support myself with my arm at elbow level. My left hand could not possibly have grasped the handle of the walker.

The two of them got me up to a standing position. I could hardly put any weight on my left leg again – not because of the stroke, but because of the sprained knee brought on by the spasms. Alex was very understanding. He could see I was trying. We took a few, laborious steps away from the bed, then he had me return to the bed in reverse. It was all I could do. Walking backward was surprisingly difficult. I had to lean hard on the walker and on Louis to keep my balance.

I was disappointed in my inabilities. At one point I said to Alex and Louis, "I feel like I'm letting you guys down." That gave them a chuckle. Alex assured me I was doing fine. He could see my left leg's biggest issue was the sprained knee, not the stroke. He restated his certainty I would recover fully, although he cautioned it might take a year or more.

Then I discovered another common aftereffect of stroke. I became absurdly emotional. These two young guys were showing such compassion, such support and kindness, that I got all choked up. It took great effort not to sob uncontrollably. Good grief, this was weird and embarrassing. I'm kind of an emotional fellow to begin with, but this was bizarre.

Thankfully, one of the doctors had explained this to me before I became so emotional with Alex and Louis, so I was able to tell them what was going on. I didn't want them to think I was a goofball who routinely burst into tears. The condition has a name. It's called emotional incontinence, and it's common after brain damage.

Some medical terms are remarkably apt. I knew the word "incontinence," of course, but had not really thought about what the term means. The literal definition is "inability to contain." An incontinent person is unable to contain their bladder. An *emotionally* incontinent person is unable to contain their emotions.

Frequently, while I was in the hospital and for many months after, the slightest things would cause wildly exaggerated emotional responses. TV shows that were moderately funny at best would elicit gigantic guffaws I couldn't control. A sentimental moment would bring a big lump to my throat and tears to my eyes.

Sometimes, the two responses happened simultaneously. While watching *How The Grinch Stole Christmas* six months after the stroke, I got all choked up at the part where Boris Karloff says the Grinch's heart "...grew three sizes that day...." Within seconds, I was practically sobbing. "That's such a wonderful story!" I blurted out. "It never gets old."

It is a wonderful story, and I do get sentimental every

time I watch it, but I was sobbing uncontrollably. My crazy, overly-emotional response became amusing after a few minutes. I began to laugh at myself, even as I was still sobbing over the Grinch, who had "...found the strength of ten Grinches, plus two!" Soon I was howling with laughter and bursting out sobs at the same time. Laughing wildly while simultaneously crying was altogether new to me. Emotional incontinence is weird.

Then I faced a new predicament – I couldn't breathe. The laughing and sobbing were so out of control, I started gasping for breath. My face turned red. I felt dizzy, and stars began to appear before my eyes. If I didn't pull myself together, I was going to pass out! Thankfully, I calmed down in time to start breathing normally again. Emotional incontinence is one of several stroke-induced effects I knew nothing about before, but now it is annoyingly familiar.

Alex exuded unwavering encouragement and kindness. Although I only saw him a few times while I was in the hospital, his thoughtful reassurance in each therapy session did as much to help me psychologically as physically.

The remainder of that Wednesday was relatively uneventful. At one point, a nurse came in to inspect the heart monitors attached to my chest. One of my spasms hit right then, causing my knee to jerk up so fast it almost bonked her on the chin as she leaned over me. I consciously focused on my left leg's hamstring and told it to settle down. It worked. With focus, I could enable some control over the spasms. This was significant, and I knew it. My brain still had a little authority over my left leg. I continued to focus while the nurse administered her test. Unfortunately, I discovered I could not keep this up at night while trying to sleep.

~ ~ ~ ~

Thursday was July Fourth. Colleene and I had developed a routine by then. She came in around 9:00 AM, fed me breakfast, then fetched us fresh coffees from the service area down the hall. I'd had another bad night of too many spasms and not enough sleep. She let me doze off while she doodled on her smartphone.

In the afternoon, we watched the national Independence Day Celebration broadcast from Washington, DC. Thank goodness for TV. People must have gone stir crazy in hospitals before. Since I couldn't go anywhere for the holiday, it was wonderful to have a festive program to watch.

My dad came in to visit in the evening. The three of us watched fireworks from the large window in the hospital room. My room was on the third floor, and Transmountain Hospital, as its name implies, is on Transmountain Road, so we had a good view of El Paso's west side. In the distance we saw several fireworks shows going on at once. Some of the nurses wore colorful ribbons or hats with their hospital scrubs. It was as pleasant a Fourth Of July as I could have expected, under the circumstances.

Colleene and my dad stayed until almost 10:00, when the last of the fireworks shows ended. I had another night of gruesome spasms, although they were spaced out more than on previous nights, allowing me to get a few hours of sleep.

Colleene and I repeated our morning rituals when she came in Friday morning. By then we had started discussions with the doctors about where I was to go next and what treatment I would need. Some insisted I go straight from the hospital to a physical therapy rehabilitation facility – a prospect I did not find at all appealing. Others were open to the possibility I could return home.

I understood the importance of physical therapy. Regaining the use of my left arm and leg would not happen without it. That was clear to me. But spending weeks away from home for one or two hours of therapy per day seemed excessive. I knew myself, and I knew how resolved I was to get my life back. Finding the discipline to exercise would not require prodding from a therapist, which is a large part of a therapist's job. Besides, I simply could not afford that much care.

Around mid-morning of that Friday, I found out just how little I could afford more care. A pleasant, business-like woman came in for a visit. She was from the hospital's billing office. She brought the invoice for the treatment I had received so far. My six days of hospital care and tests came to an astounding total of $72,000, and that did not include doctor's fees.

Gasp! Here's what's wrong with health care! Being in a hospital costs twelve thousand dollars *per day*? That works out to five hundred dollars per hour, every hour, 24/7. I could charter a luxury yacht and take a dozen friends on a cruise for less.

The care I received from Providence Transmountain was stellar. Priscilla, Alex, Jennifer, and all the other fine specialists who looked after me deserve to make good incomes. I don't fault any of the hospital staff for the vulgar over-charging that goes on in the medical field. I also don't claim to have a solution for the way we pay for medical care in the USA, but I will assert that five hundred bucks per hour is ten times more than exorbitant.

I was already somewhat woozy from lack of sleep. The dollar amount of my hospital bill made my eyes go out of focus. It would take ten years to pay that off, and there would be many more expenses to come. Then the pleasant, business-like woman informed me the hospital was allowing a substantial self-pay discount on my bill. Further, I could pay the bill over a three-year period. I felt as if I had been saved from drowning.

The hospital's offer was a wonderful relief, but it brought up another concern. If the hospital could reduce my charges so much, since I was paying my own bill, how much do they try to over-charge insurance? Perhaps, after recovering from the stroke, it's time for me to become a more active participant in the political discussion about healthcare costs. Turning our entire healthcare system over to the federal government is absolutely not the answer, but there must be a better way than how it's done now. People in The United Kingdom used to worship their National Health Service. They even featured it in the 2012 Summer Olympic Games ceremony in London. It was terrific for a few decades, but now Britain's NHS is falling apart. Costs are skyrocketing, nurses and doctors are leaving the program by the thousands. There must be a better way.

Two nurses came in to see me after lunch. They checked my vitals, as usual. Then they asked a bunch of questions about how I was feeling. They asked Colleene how well prepared she was to assist my recovery. Colleene felt, as I did, that sending me to a rehabilitation facility was unnecessary. However, she was worried I might be too much for her to handle, especially for the first few weeks. The nurses typed notes into a portable computer station. They told us Dr. Rao was deciding when to release me and where to send me next.

Twenty minutes later, one of the nurses returned with the news the hospital would release me that very afternoon. I was heading home.

Leaving a hospital is not like checking out of a hotel. I could not simply take off as soon as they told me I was being released. Charts and records needed finalizing, and they would arrange for an ambulance to transport me to the house for no additional charge. That was a big relief to Colleene and me. I could hardly get from the bed to a wheelchair, even with ample assistance. Standing up outside in the parking lot and hoisting my limp left side into a car with only Colleene to help seemed impossible.

With a few hours left before my release, I had time for another visit from Alex and Louis. I gave it my best effort, but still could not put more than the slightest weight on my left leg. My sprained knee needed to heal before it would support weight. Alex could see I wasn't faking or exaggerating the pain. My knee was badly swollen.

Alex and Louis were again so kind and reassuring that they triggered my emotional incontinence. At one point, as I was struggling to hold back wild sobs, I asked Alex again if he was familiar with the condition. This had happened Wednesday, and I felt very self-conscious. Yes, he confirmed that he understood it well. "Good," I said, "so you won't think I'm weird for telling you, I love you, man!" That brought a good chuckle from everyone in the room.

Alex and Louis stressed their confidence that I would regain normal use of my left limbs, although it may take a year or more. They emphasized that, compared to other patients they worked with, I was still plenty young and healthy. What an encouraging thing to tell me, particularly since I was feeling older and more feeble than ever before. They walked me around the room as much as my swollen knee would allow. Then Louis left as Alex sat me in a chair for some stretching exercises.

Before Alex said his final good-bye, he asked if I would mind if he prayed with me. I'm not a religious person, but I certainly would not decline such a meaningful gesture. I beckoned Colleene to join us. Alex put his hand on my shoulder and offered a very thoughtful prayer for my recovery. I was sobbing as he bade us farewell. Emotional incontinence aside, Alex's sincere caring touched me deeply.

Jennifer also came in for one last session of occupational therapy. She was visibly upset by the news that I was being released that afternoon. Like Alex, Jennifer genuinely cares about the people she assists. She seemed worried that I might not be ready for release from care. Her concern was touching, and I told her so with sincere thanks. I offered my best assurance that I would continue therapy. I pleaded with her to let me go home and not to worry about me. I really did not want to be in a hospital any longer.

With it being our last session, Jennifer demonstrated several movements I could use to strengthen my hand on my own. It clearly concerned her, like a mother sending a child off for the first day of school, that I was leaving her care, that she would not be looking after me anymore.

Around 4:30, a two-person ambulance crew entered my room with a gurney. Departure time had arrived. Colleene quickly gathered my belongings, including my laptop computer, which had remained in its case for the entirety of my hospital stay. How silly I felt, six days and a stroke later, to have thought I would occupy my time with a computer while in the hospital. Colleene also took a wheelchair and a walker down to the car – aids the hospital was giving me. Colleene needed three trips to get all my stuff down to the car. Then she headed on home while the man and woman ambulance crew maneuvered me onto the gurney.

Just when they loaded and secured me onto the gurney, a woman came into the room to deliver my dinner. The ambulance crew offered to wait, if I wanted to eat before we left. That was very nice of them, but I was eager to get home. I hoped the somewhat confused staff woman didn't mind as I politely declined the dinner she offered.

The ambulance duo rolled me through the labyrinth of hospital hallways and elevators. When we exited the hospital doors, I was immediately jolted back into the reality of a July afternoon in El Paso. It was over a hundred degrees outside, and the brightness of the sun was too much for my eyes. I couldn't remember a time I had spent six straight days indoors.

Hospitals work their air conditioners hard. This is not a complaint; I like it nice and cool, but I am not accustomed to wanting extra blankets during a West Texas summer. While in the hospital room, I requested additional covers until I was up to four extra blankets. I once asked a nurse about the cool temperature in the hospital. She told me it helped keep germs from spreading. They would keep the temperature below freezing if they could, but that would be unworkable.

Seeing the interior of an ambulance was another first for me. It was not as elaborate with high tech devices as I imagined. The ambulance seemed stark and utilitarian on the inside. Perhaps I didn't know what to look for.

When we got to the house, Colleene's whole family was waiting to receive me. Ever the jokester, I called out, "Honey, I'm home!" as the EMTs rolled me up the driveway.

4 Relearning The Basics Of Life

The ambulance team rolled me into the house, but the gurney was too bulky to make the tight turns down the hall to the front bedroom. Colleene and her daughter-in-law had moved a dresser out of the front bedroom to allow a path for a wheelchair. The EMTs lowered the gurney and assisted me into my new wheelchair. Once in the wheelchair, I could not propel myself, because my left hand felt like a glove full of sand. My left arm had the strength of an overcooked egg noodle. They rolled me to the front bedroom and assisted me into bed.

Before departing, the ambulance crew offered more welcome encouragement. As Alex and Jennifer had told me at the hospital, these two EMTs, who had only spent an hour with me, said they expected me to make a full recovery. It would likely take several months and lots of effort, but they had seen people like me return to full lives.

Sensing Colleene's worry that I might be more than she could manage, they made a point to tell us both we could handle this. The hardest part for Colleene would be helping me move around for the first few weeks. If she couldn't handle it, they'd gladly come back and transport me to a rehabilitation center.

The ambulance duo made sure I was secure in my bed and all was well before heading out. I heard them load the gurney back into the ambulance, then the grinding diesel engine faded as they drove away. Suddenly it was very quiet. I was home. Even with six people under one roof, this was a tranquil haven compared to a hospital.

Returning home was wonderful, but right away I missed the convenience of the motorized hospital bed. Sitting up in a regular bed required tremendous effort and lots of help from Colleene. We immediately started learning tricks for moving me around.

~ ~ ~ ~

Living with Colleene was supposed to be temporary. She had moved with me from Reno, Nevada, to El Paso a few months after my mother died. Before Mom passed away, my dad had given me his parents' house. The house had sat vacant for years and needed a ton of repairs. My dad figured I could renovate it and sell it or rent it out. Fixing it up was too big a project for him to take on.

After Mom died, I was concerned Dad might need my help. Since I then owned a house in El Paso, I began considering moving back to my home town, something I once thought I would never do.

My thoughts of moving back to Texas prompted Colleene to take an interest in El Paso, too. She did a little internet research and discovered houses in El Paso cost much less than in Reno. She could sell her house in Reno and buy a bigger, nicer house in El Paso with her cash equity. That would allow her to provide a spacious home for her disabled son, his wife, and their two young sons, who were living in an apartment in Reno.

So it was Colleene who actually got the process started for all of us relocating to El Paso. She contacted a real estate agent in Reno and asked him to evaluate her house. The agent told her confidently the house would sell for thirty thousand dollars *more* than her desired price. Papers were signed, pictures were taken, and a date was set for the house to go on the market. She did all this while I was out of town on a job.

Two hours after the house officially became available, a buyer offered twelve thousand dollars more than the asking price. Remember, the asking price was already thirty thousand more than Colleene thought her house would sell for. In less than a day, Colleene's house sold for forty-one thousand dollars *more* than the original amount she would have been happy with. Time to move!

In El Paso she bought a nice house on the city's west side. Her new home was twice the size of her house in Reno, and it included a splendid view from the back yard, yet it cost substantially less than her house in Reno had sold for. You know what they say about real estate: Location, location, location. Honestly, I don't get why the

Jarvis Hooten

Reno housing market was so explosive. Colleene sold her house just as the market was peaking. That's the fourth rule of real estate: Timing.

The way I fit into the scenario with Colleene and her family was intended to be temporary. I helped the five of them move to El Paso. We made a nice trip of it, taking in the Grand Canyon along the way. The plan was for me to stay with them while my grandparents' former house was renovated, then I would take up residence there. From the beginning, the plan was for me to live in my own house.

Perhaps that was more explanation than you cared to know, but there is the back story to my living situation. We had barely moved into Colleene's new house and got the furniture arranged when I had the stroke. Her move-in date was June 15. I went to the hospital on June 29.

There I was on Friday, July 5th, 2019, having just come home from the hospital. I would need a year or more of recovery before I could even think about resuming renovations to my grandparents' house. I was totally dependent on Colleene. She never uttered a word of complaint, never made me feel like a burden.

~ ~ ~ ~

Our first trial came within an hour after the ambulance crew left. It was dinner time. The food at Providence Hospital had been quite agreeable, as I have described, but dinner in a hospital room can't compete with dinner at home.

First, we had to figure out where I could eat. We had a recliner next to the bed. Perhaps Colleene could sit there and feed me in bed? No, it was too far to reach. Half of each meal would end up on the floor. Besides, sitting up in bed required considerable effort and half a dozen pillows, and then I was still unstable. We decided I should get out of bed and sit in the recliner. Then I could eat meals from a TV tray table. Transferring my bulk from bed to chair would be a challenge, but it seemed the best option. We needed to figure this out for upcoming days, anyway. Might as well start learning how to move me around that very evening.

The bed was on a pedestal with a thick mattress, so it was higher than the recliner. I could practically fall from the bed into the chair, and I would have been game to try that, but merely sitting up was more than I could do on my own. Colleene planted her feet next to the bed and held out her arm. With my right hand, I grasped her wrist and had to pull hard to bring myself up to a sitting position. Then she helped me stand up on my good leg.

Standing up was unexpectedly unnerving. Here's an element of post-stroke existence I did not anticipate: fear. Losing the use of half one's body is scary in ways that none of us can understand, until it happens to us. My left leg was useless. If I lost my balance while standing on my right leg, there was nothing to stop me from falling. The simple act of rising from a chair had suddenly become frightening.

Since the recliner was close to the bed, I didn't have to stay standing for long. Once I was upright, I pivoted on my right foot, did a few heel-toe shuffle steps while leaning hard on Colleene, and sat down heavily on the chair. Having a stroke stinks.

Once settled into the recliner, I enjoyed a satisfying

home meal. Colleene cut everything to bite sizes, allowing me to eat comfortably with my right hand. This became our routine for almost two months. Colleene carried meals to the front bedroom, having first cut the food into bite sizes. I only ate twice a day – a late breakfast and early dinner. Nonetheless, feeding me was a lot of extra effort for Colleene. Suffering a stroke would have been unthinkably worse, had I been without such a thoughtful, attentive caregiver.

Okay, that took care of my fuel intake. Everything that burns fuel puts out exhaust. After dinner, we discussed my number one and number two options for, you know, going Number One and Number Two. That's a conversation no one wants to have, but it was one of the things we had to work out. Bodily functions become complicated ordeals after a stroke.

We had brought home two urine bottles from the hospital. Here's an advantage I willingly admit we men have; it's a lot easier for us to pee. I don't know how a woman relieves herself in bed, other than with a bedpan, which I imagine would be uncomfortable and unavoidably messy. With male plumbing, solving my Number One problem was a cinch. As an extra precaution, we stood the urine bottles in a bucket next to the bed. I couldn't bear the thought of asking Colleene to mop up a puddle of my pee, thus the bucket provided security against knocking over a disgusting jug of urine.

Using a urine bottle was simple while I sat in the recliner. The bucket was easy to reach from the chair with my right hand. Once in bed, however, I could not reach the urine bottles. Also (pardon me if this is too much information), I could not hold the bottle in place while, um, maintaining my aim. That required two hands, one to hold the jug and the other to hold my ding-a-ling. Only one of my hands worked. Colleene, bless the woman, held a urine bottle for me each time I needed to pee in bed for almost two months. Even in the middle of the night, she insisted on waking up to assist me. If I got the urge at 3:00 AM, I'd apologetically nudge her, and she'd hop right up and fetch a urine bottle. If I tried to reach a bottle on my own without disturbing her, she always sensed my movement. She convinced me to wake her and not try to use a urine bottle on my own, because, she conceded, she didn't much like the idea of mopping up my pee, either.

That took care of the easy part. For the other "job," the hospital had sent home a potty chair. I hope never to use one of those again. Having a bowel movement on a little stool in a bedroom is demoralizing. Portable potty seats are small and wobbly. I never so appreciated the sturdiness of a good toilet. Also, when using a standard toilet, our smelly stuff drops into water. It smells bad on the way down, but once in the water, the stench no longer drifts out through the air. When I used the potty chair, my poop sat in the bucket, exposed to the air and releasing unbearable stink for several minutes. The entire bedroom – no, the entire front of the house – smelled bad enough to make people's eyes water. Then, adding to the indignity, poor Colleene had to carry my bucket of excrement out of the room, dump it in the toilet, and clean out the bucket.

We only did this routine twice before coming up with

a better solution. The reason for using the potty chair in the first place was I could not fit into Colleene's bathroom in my wheelchair. It occurred to me the wheelchair would fit into the hall bathroom. We had not intended to use that bathroom, not wanting to impose on other members of the household, but Colleene's grandsons were happy to share access.

The first time we tried using the hall bathroom was something of a comedy routine. Remember, for over a month, I could not stand up on my own. I could not move from bed to wheelchair without significant help. Once in the wheelchair, I could not propel myself. My left hand and left arm were useless.

All those factors meant Colleene had to help, and help a lot, to transport me to the hall bathroom and onto the toilet. Once in the bathroom, we strapped a belt around my chest, and she pulled that with all her might to stand me up. She held on while I stabilized my balance on one foot, then I did my shuffle step from the wheelchair to the toilet. This maneuver scared the hell out of us every time. I still weighed over 250 pounds. If I had lost my balance, I could have toppled over on Colleene, causing both of us to fall into the tub and break several bones.

Bowel movements required extensive advance planning. Waiting for the usual urge to use the toilet would not do, because by then it would be too late. I had to get to the toilet long before the urge struck, then wait.

The effort was worth it. What a relief to relieve myself as a normal person. I now recognize toilets are among the most underappreciated conveniences of modern life. Like refrigerators and cell phones, we don't give toilets a second thought until we are without them, and we forget they are relatively recent inventions. Indoor plumbing was still a novelty merely a century ago. Outhouses were disgusting, even for healthy, ambulatory people. Imagine a stroke victim trying to access one of those smelly little sheds. Horrible. I feel fortunate that I never had an "accident." Eewww, it's vile to think about.

That covers the subject of how we managed my bodily functions. I didn't want to spend too much time on such an unappealing topic, but the issue had to be addressed. All animals have to pee and poop. Having a stroke or other illness makes us recognize the luxury of something so basic as a toilet.

Priscilla and the other night nurses at Providence Transmountain Hospital had been delightful, but it sure was nice to sleep through a night without being awakened every two hours. My sleep was not entirely without interruption, however. The wretched spasms continued to jolt me out of my slumber. Sometimes the intense contractions were twenty minutes apart, sometimes two minutes apart. As in the hospital, the contractions were so sudden and extreme that, after each spasm passed, I would feel profoundly relaxed. This was how I was able to sleep. Each eruption of my hamstring jerked me awake with a shock of searing pain, such that I sometimes howled and woke up Colleene. Incredibly, when the contractions relaxed, so did I, and I'd be back asleep in seconds.

By 3:00 AM the spasms usually declined or stopped altogether, allowing me at least a few hours of unbroken snooze time. Regardless, a good night of steady, pain-free sleep would be months away. I took lots of naps over the summer of 2019.

Naps were a pleasant way to pass the time. Within the first two days at home, it became clear my life was to be quite uneventful for a while. Simply getting me out of bed and dressed took an hour. Breakfast used up another hour, and then there was a trip down the hall to the john – one more hour gone.

Modern technology kept me company. I was able to sit at my computer desk in the wheelchair. Typing one-handed was slow and awkward, but it was wonderful to exchange e-mails with friends. Talking with old friends was therapeutic. A cell phone, computer, and TV were my companions for several months – those and Colleene, of course.

One particularly important phone chat was with my cousin, Sharon, daughter of my Uncle Lloyd. She explained something I had not known. One of the reasons Uncle Lloyd never recovered from his stroke was he lost hope; he gave up. The stroke and some other discouraging factors in his life defeated his motivation. Sharon was convinced Lloyd could have regained what the stroke took from him, had he only tried harder.

She pressed that message hard, and it stuck. I resolved to stay motivated. I may never fully recover from the stroke, but I would try. I would not spend the rest of my life as an invalid.

5 It's All About Therapy ... And Therapists

After a weekend of adjusting to the new status quo, it was time to begin my new job – recovery. Monday we called a service the hospital had recommended. It was an in-home care business with funding assistance from the state, so they could offer a discount to uninsured saps like me. That very afternoon, a nurse made a house call to take my vitals and set me up in the program.

Two days later – Wednesday, July 10, 2019 – I received my first in-home visit from a physical therapist. His name was Brandon, a name that from that day forward will always strike fear into my heart. Brandon was my only bad experience with a physical therapist, and it was really, really bad. This part is hard to write about. That Wednesday afternoon was so brutal, I prefer not to think about it, but the story should be told.

When Brandon arrived, I was at my computer. I had found helpful information about stroke-related spasms, and I started to ask him about it. (Info on spasms is woefully lacking, both on the internet and from every doctor I have spoken with.) Brandon's first words to me were, "Well, let's not get carried away with our little internet searches. *I'm* the one you need to listen to."

In a few seconds, he'd shown himself to be rude, arrogant, and uninterested in responding to my questions. Okay, I get it; people in medical professions get tired of patients bringing up stuff they read on the internet. That does not mean they can shoot us down when we have a legitimate concern. Most medical professionals *encouraged* me to seek answers on the internet. The more I could learn on my own, the less I needed them to explain every little thing to me.

Brandon's attitude was I shouldn't concern myself with "little internet searches." *Little* internet searches? The internet is the greatest resource of information in history, yet he's the only one I should listen to? This was my introduction to the horror named Brandon.

Before we started, he demanded we rearrange the bedroom furniture. "You should take that desk out," he ordered. Colleene and I explained that removing the desk would be excessively burdensome. It was a big, heavy desk, which had to be disassembled to get through the bedroom door. Further, I pleaded, I was in no condition to move furniture. I began to explain the struggle I was having with leg spasms; that the spasms had apparently sprained my knee.

"We gotta get you past that right off," he interrupted, and instructed me to stand up.

My left knee was swollen to double its normal size, and I was wearing shorts. Anyone could see the knee was in a state of distress. That didn't register with Brandon. He did help me stand up, but he immediately grew impatient that I could not straighten my left leg.

"You need to put your foot down. Go ahead. I can hold you up." We had wrapped a belt around my chest, a common practice for physical therapy. He jerked the belt to demonstrate his grip.

Being held up was not the problem. Straightening my left leg caused knife-stabbing pain to the knee. Putting weight on that leg caused screaming-in-agony pain.

We stood there for a moment – me balancing on my right leg, holding my left leg up with the knee slightly bent and him deciding what to do with me next. He had me sit back down on the wheelchair. Then he crouched in front of me. I thought he was at last going to take the knee seriously.

No, he took hold of my left ankle and pulled my leg up, pushing down on the knee. He was forcing me to straighten out that leg. I howled with pain.

"I see. You must have a low tolerance for pain." What a goddamn jackass. Now he's calling me a wimp.

At the time, I didn't know better. I thought he was a professional; he must know what he's doing. I must be a wimp.

He stood up and stated, "Man, we gotta get you moving *now*. I should have you up on the bed on your hands and knees, stretching and moving around. This has to start now." He smacked his right fist into the palm of his left hand for emphasis. "You should be up and walking *today*."

Colleene had heard enough. "If that's true," she said, trying to remain calm, "then obviously something else besides the stroke is wrong. His knee is way too swollen. There has to be some other kind of problem." My savior came to my rescue. In my condition, I did not have the wherewithal to confront this beast. Colleene is one of the most passive, tolerant people I know. But when she gets ticked off, especially if a jerk is abusing someone she cares about, she can be a little scary. Brandon regarded her for a moment, then looked back at me.

"Yeah, maybe you should get that knee checked out before we try any more therapy." First and only reasonable thing he said. "I guess we can't do much more today. I'll check back later in the week." I felt as if I had escaped the jaws of a shark. The torture, abuse, and insults were over.

I was still at the very beginning stage of recovery. I didn't know then how utterly wrong Brandon was. I thought he – or someone like him – must be what I was condemned to endure for the next year or so. I'd heard physical therapy could be brutal. Could it really be *this* barbaric? Were all therapists so savage? At the hospital, Alex and Jennifer had seemed quite compassionate and considerate. Were they the outliers of physical therapy? Or was Brandon the exception?

It was late afternoon when Brandon left. I was too exhausted to contemplate what I had just been through. I looked at Colleene. Bless the woman – she validated what

I was thinking. "That guy was a jerk. There's no way you could be crawling around on all fours doing the stuff he was talking about! We need to get your knee checked out before you do any more physical therapy."

She helped me into the recliner, which allowed me to sit with my knee at a comfortable angle. I was spent. I leaned the chair back and conked out for a comforting nap.

An hour later, Colleene woke me up to start our dinner routine. This began with adjusting me to a sitting position and situating a tray-stand in front of the recliner. She brought dinner back to me, then she went out to sit with the family for her dinner. I ate my pre-cut bites while mindlessly watching TV.

My thoughts returned to dark places. Was the torture I'd suffered that afternoon going to become my routine for the next year, maybe longer? I'd promised my cousin Sharon I would stay motivated, that I'd stick to my therapy, even if it was tough. I hadn't known it could possibly be so gruesome. I tried to tell myself to buck up, push through the pain; grisly therapy was my only option. I had to find the courage to endure the likes of Brandon.

Later that night, the spasms came back worse than ever. They tended to start shortly after I went to bed. Lying down apparently stretched the hamstring in a way that triggered contractions. The pain was out of this world. I often had to clap my right hand over my mouth, lest I bellow out a wail that would alarm the entire household. My knee was in agony. Each contraction injured the swollen joint more than it already was, but I couldn't stop the spasms.

Jarvis Hooten

My mind went back to that awful place it had visited on my third night in the hospital. I couldn't withstand this for a year. Even if I found the courage to endure the torment of physical therapy, the rest of my life wasn't worth it. I was ready to trade all the years I had left for the year of torture I was facing. A few more decades of being alive were not worth a year of Brandon's torment. This time, unlike that night in the hospital, these dark thoughts extended to considering methods to end myself. Sitting in my car with the engine running in the garage seemed clean and efficient.

Looking back on that night, it really ticks me off that Brandon pushed me to the edge like that. Maybe he meant well. Maybe he saw I was a big guy, as he was, and I wasn't terribly old, so he thought some drill-sergeant type abuse was what I needed for motivation. Maybe he had no idea how damaging his behavior was.

On the other hand, if he abuses elderly ladies the way he mistreated me, Brandon needs to find another line of work. Physical therapy is not the right profession for an abusive blockhead.

Next morning, after one of the most distressing nights of my life, I woke up to a solid new sense of awareness. A few hours sleep were enough to inspire fresh confidence. I boldly determined that Brandon was wrong. Physical therapy should not be torture. Some might call it torture, but excruciating pain is a clear sign that something is amiss. Therapy, like exercise, should only push a person's comfort envelope, not drive them into unworldly torment. PT might be a bit uncomfortable. It should not be sheer agony.

Feeling lucid and courageous, I told Colleene I was done with Brandon. We needed to find a different solution. I could do physical therapy on my own, if I had to. I'd return to my "little internet searches," as Brandon had condescended, to learn what to do. Also, I was beginning to believe I should submit to another hospital visit to have my knee checked out. The pain was becoming intolerable, and it was prohibiting any chance for rehabilitation.

An elephant-sized knee wasn't my only worry. The swelling in my hand had become alarming, too. My fingers were like bratwursts.

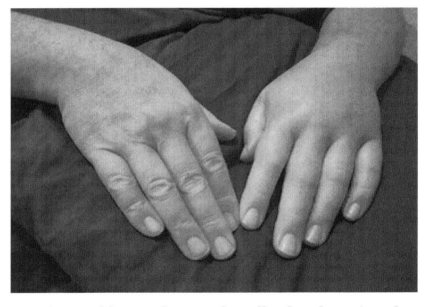

The troublesome knee and swollen hand continued to worsen through the day. Colleene agreed another hospital trip was in order, but how to get me there? She was concerned I could fall while getting into the car. Was my situation serious enough to warrant an ambulance?

By Saturday morning I couldn't take it anymore. I even dismissed my concern over insurance. I persuaded Colleene I could get into the car without falling, and I wanted to go that very day. We'd go to the county hospital, uninsured indigent that I was, and find out what could be done about my afflicted knee and swollen hand.

I skipped breakfast that morning, thinking the hospital might want to do blood work. Colleene helped me get dressed. I hadn't put on a full set of clothes since the day I went to Transmountain Hospital two weeks earlier.

When Colleene rolled me out to the car, for a moment, I thought she might be right about the perils of this plan. From a wheelchair, my mid-sized SUV looked like a monster truck. The passenger seat towered above me. How would I possibly climb up to that precipice?

Colleene's son came out to help. The two of them hoisted me up to standing. I balanced precariously on my right leg as Brian reached behind me and heaved my limp left leg into the car. Then I was able to drop my rear onto the edge of the seat. With several jostles and jerks, I was in and ready to go. I hated being such an invalid.

We didn't go to Providence Hospital this time. I had accepted the embarrassment that I was an uninsured indigent, reliant on the assistance of taxpayers. El Paso's county-supported hospital is called University Medical Center. Colleene pulled up to the emergency entrance and went inside. About ninety seconds later, a male nurse came out to the car with a wheelchair. He helped me from the car into the wheelchair and rolled me right past the waiting area to an examining room. Same as at Transmountain Hospital, a patient who shows up talking of stroke jumps to the head of the line.

A nurse met us in the examining room and took my vitals. Moments later, a physician's assistant came in and raced through a list of questions. Neither Colleene nor I had said I was having a stroke. We were clear that I'd *had* a stroke, but other issues needed some follow-up examination. Once she understood that, the physician's assistant dropped me back to the end of the line. She didn't say that in so many words. It was more a polite, "Since you're not having a stroke at the moment, we'll move you to the waiting room until a doctor is available."

An orderly rolled me to a pleasant waiting area. It was 11:00 AM, Saturday, July 13, 2019. The outside temperature was over 100 degrees. Colleene and I had dressed for the hot weather. I wore shorts and a polo shirt; she wore a light summer outfit. The hospital interior was no more than sixty degrees. Within a half hour we asked an orderly if we could have a few blankets. It seemed luxurious, at first, to be in a cool waiting room on a West Texas summer day, but after thirty minutes we were freezing!

I don't know if I'd have the patience to do for Colleene what she's done for me. That day at UMC was an example of her steadfast care. We had skipped breakfast. I thought the hospital might do blood work, which they did, and they usually want patients not to eat before having blood drawn, so I had gone without my morning meal. Colleene skipped breakfast because she always skips breakfast. By 1:00 PM, both of us were becoming hungry, and that turned out to be just the start of our wait. Being an uninsured indigent means long waits for non-emergency medical care.

Wrapped up in blankets in the very cool waiting room allowed us both to pass some of the time napping. The hospital wheelchair was not very comfortable, yet somehow it held my leg in an ideal position to prevent spasms. Without those horrible spasms, I could sleep better sitting up in a wheelchair than at home in bed.

At around 3:00 PM, Colleene walked to the nurse's station to check my status. The nurse politely apologized for our long wait, but there were still several patients ahead of me. She assured Colleene they hadn't forgotten about us.

There was a TV in the waiting room. It was set to a Spanish language station. I speak a little Spanish, as does anyone who grew up in El Paso, but not enough to follow a TV show. All Colleene and I could do to pass the time was chat, snooze, and people watch.

Watching people became particularly interesting twice that afternoon. Armed sheriff's deputies escorted handcuffed men in orange jumpsuits past the waiting area. This was the county hospital, where officers took prison inmates who needed medical attention.

More hours passed. At 7:00 PM, I urged Colleene to go get something to eat. I knew she must have been starving. She would not leave me alone at the hospital. I should just shut up about it. She was fine, she insisted.

At almost 10:00 PM, a staff person came in and asked me to confirm my full name and birthdate. This is standard procedure for establishing a person's identity, I've learned. After our eleven-hour wait, things started happening quickly. The orderly hustled me into a hospital room and transferred me to the bed. A nurse installed an IV port into my right arm while another nurse checked my vital signs again. A pleasant looking, surprisingly young doctor swept in and asked me to restate my reason for coming in.

"I had a stroke two weeks ago," I explained. I spoke slowly and deliberately to overcome my speech detriment. "Since then I've had a terrible time with spasms, which I think sprained my knee. My left hand is badly swollen. A physical therapist came by the house a couple of days ago. When he straightened out my left leg, it caused intense pain. I want to find out if my knee is sprained, if there's something I can do about the spasms, and if the swelling in my left hand is something to worry about."

"Well, that sizes things up nicely," the doctor replied. He looked under the sheet at my left knee. "Oh yeah, that's not right. Let's get that x-rayed," he said to a nurse.

Minutes later, a technician rolled an impressive electronic device into the room. Very gingerly, he lifted my left leg enough to slide a square plate underneath the knee. Unlike Brandon, these medical people recognized something was clearly wrong with the knee, and they were gentle with it. After imaging the knee, he moved the plate onto my chest and gingerly placed my left hand on it. A few taps on a computer keyboard, and he was done. That's all it took to get x-rays of my knee and hand. I didn't have to get out of bed or hardly move. Modern technology is glorious.

Two minutes after the portable x-ray technician left, a woman strolled in pushing another complex device on wheels – a portable ultrasound machine. She applied goop to my left bicep, then spent a good twenty minutes pressing and dragging a smooth probe up and down my arm.

The hospital room was a whirlwind of activity for about half an hour. Then it was suddenly quiet, and Colleene and I were in wait mode again.

Around 11:00 PM, the pleasant doctor came back in with lots of news. The x-ray verified my knee was undeniably sprained. I should not put weight on it or try to straighten it out until the swelling went down. Physical therapy was important, he stressed, perhaps trying to defend Brandon's improper treatment, but my left knee needed to rest and repair before I attempted exercising that leg.

The swelling in my left hand was concerning, but the ultrasound of my arm revealed no clots or other issues. I should continue massaging the hand and doing whatever exercises I could to stimulate blood flow. The x-ray of my left hand also showed no problems that would cause swelling. However, it revealed fairly advanced arthritis in my thumb, which is a common place arthritis develops. I thought the pain in my thumbs was carpal tunnel syndrome from too much time on computers. Now I find out I have *advanced* arthritis? Damn, it stinks to get old.

Our visit to the UMC Emergency Room took thirteen hours, but it accomplished everything we wanted. I got confirmation that my knee was, indeed, sprained. I did not have a low tolerance for pain; I had an injury. Physical therapy on my left leg needed to wait until the knee healed. The doctor specifically told me physical therapy should not cause pain. It can be uncomfortable, yes, to strain muscles and rebuild their capacity. But severe pain is not part of any physical therapy. Thank you, doctor. I will not allow torture from a physical therapist again.

We also learned the swelling in my hand was not caused by anything worrisome. The discomfort should decrease within a few days. My vital signs all checked out, blood work was good. It was time to go home and restart my recovery – with a new plan this time.

After the wrap-up from the doctor, we had to wait another twenty minutes for a nurse to remove my IV and clear me for departure, and there was paperwork to finish, of course. Another male nurse rolled me outside in a wheelchair and helped hoist me into the car.

It was after midnight when we finally got home. Getting out of the car was easier than getting into the car, so Colleene didn't bother waking up her son to help me into the house. We hungrily enjoyed leftovers from the fridge and hit the sack, exhausted.

Sunday we took it easy. I didn't do any exercises or exert myself at all. I felt drained, and I wanted a whole day not to think about being a stroke victim. That may seem silly. Obviously, it was impossible to forget about the stroke altogether. I needed help to do everything from combing my hair to using the toilet, and spasms continued to disrupt my sleep. But Colleene and I both used that Sunday to take a break from my recovery. We'd start working on that again Monday.

6 Learning To Clap With One Hand

We use our dominant sides for everything, don't we? I throw right-handed, eat, write, paint, and brush my teeth right-handed. What's the non-dominant side for, really, other than to assist the dominant side?

Losing the use of it showed me how very much I need my non-dominant side. Ever tried squeezing toothpaste onto a toothbrush with one hand? It can't be done. Something has to hold the brush while something else squeezes the tube. I can only imagine how difficult a stroke is for those who lose their dominant sides.

Worse, I can't imagine how devastating a stroke is for someone who does not have a caregiver. Colleene became my left side. For two months, she cut my food, squeezed my toothpaste, gave me refreshing sponge baths, and helped me get on and off the toilet. If you're reading this book as a stroke victim, I hope you have such a wonderful person looking after you. If you are reading this book as a caregiver, there's a special place in heaven for you.

Monday, July 15, 2019, sixteen days after the stroke, Colleene got on the phone and lined up a new physical therapy option for me. I'd go to UMC's west side campus, which had a full staff of physical therapists and a complete fitness facility. She set my consultation appointment for Wednesday. I was nervous about confronting physical therapists again after the horror of Brandon, but I held out hope these new therapists would be like Alex and Jennifer.

That Monday night was the worst night yet for spasms. Sometimes they attacked in rapid succession. An agonizing contraction would seize my leg, then another would hit before my hamstring could relax. Each spasm made me jerk violently in the bed, which often woke poor Colleene. The first few nights, she offered a sympathetic word or gently patted my shoulder while my leg contorted under me. After a week of multiple spasms every night, she simply lay there quietly as we both wished like hell the misery would end.

Tuesday morning, after such a rough night, I slept in until 10:00 AM. Colleene and I went through our normal morning routine. She helped dress me, which took half an hour. Then she helped me stand up. Balancing on my right leg, I did my one-footed heel-toe maneuver to the recliner. I was becoming well rehearsed at this little dance.

We took a breather for a few minutes before Colleene brought me coffee and juice. Breakfast was usually oatmeal or melon slices and a handful of mixed nuts. I had started the healthiest diet of my life, which would pay off with many benefits to my condition.

After breakfast, I was ready for a nap. Dozens of spasms had allowed only three or four hours of sleep the night before. Somehow, sitting up in the recliner caused the spasms to stop, so I decided to try sleeping in the chair. Propping my feet up on the recliner's footrest became uncomfortable within a few minutes. I got the idea to try positioning my office chair in front of the recliner, and I propped my feet on the seat of the chair.

It worked. For whatever reason, having my leg in that position did not trigger spasms. Soothing relaxation poured over me like hot fudge. The recliner was also right under an air conditioning vent. It might have been the coolest spot in the house. It was like being in the UMC hospital waiting room again. The outside temperature was over a hundred degrees, but I needed to pile on covers to be warm and snug.

I spent that entire Tuesday napping in the recliner. I only woke up to pee a couple of times (which I could do without leaving the recliner – yay male plumbing and urine bottles) and to have dinner. After dinner I sat up for a while and watched TV, still in the recliner. Then I slept that entire night in the recliner. It was wonderful. The night was not entirely spasm-free, but I had much more peaceful sleep than any night of the past two weeks.

By the next morning I'd been in that recliner for almost twenty-four hours straight. Having enjoyed such a restful previous day and night meant I felt energized and ready for my first day of the new physical therapy program. The respite from spasms had also reduced the swelling in my knee. I could almost straighten out my left leg and put a little weight on it. It was going to be a good day.

Transporting a person who can't walk or push his own wheelchair requires a lot of planning and extra effort. I looked into handicapped van services and other options. Some ride share companies like Uber and Lyft offer wheelchair access vehicles, but they had not started those in El Paso yet. Colleene was worried she wouldn't be able to handle getting me into and out of our SUV. We'd managed it okay for the trip to the county hospital, but we had extra help at both ends of the trip. At the physical therapy clinic, she'd have to haul me out of the car by herself. She was especially concerned I might fall while we were away from the house.

Arranging a ride service was complicated and expensive – one of many peripheral predicaments attached to stroke recovery. Losing our basic ambulatory function, becoming unable to move about freely, changes everything about daily life. Like during a power outage or losing a cell phone, we don't appreciate how much we use something until it's gone. I've never felt so helpless, so utterly dependent on others. Deciding on a method for transporting me around was an unexpected additional stress.

I spent three days researching transportation options. I decided my SUV was the best solution. Then I had to convince Colleene. She went along with my decision, but not without ample apprehension. The UMC West facility was only about ten minutes from the house.

Knowing it would soothe Colleene's stress, I made no complaint when she wanted to leave the house forty-five minutes ahead of time.

She was right to be concerned, of course. Hoisting me into the car from the wheelchair was treacherous for the first few weeks. Thank goodness we both have senses of humor. We had to stop and laugh at ourselves on several occasions. Sometimes I'd get stuck halfway into the car, and I'd have to hold an awkward pose for a few minutes while we figured out how to get me unstuck. Better to laugh than curse, although cursing sometimes helped, too.

When we arrived at the clinic, Colleene pulled up to the entrance, hopped out, and retrieved the wheelchair from the back. The wheelchair was heavy and bulky. I could do nothing but sit in the passenger seat as she struggled with it. She rolled the wheelchair around to the passenger side and helped heave me out of the car. She pushed me into the clinic, so I wasn't left sitting in the scorching West Texas sun, then she hustled back outside to park the car. This was the routine for taking me anywhere for three months after the stroke.

The first person to work with me at the clinic was an occupational therapist named Elsa. The trick she offered for remembering her name was to think of the movie *Frozen*. I might not have got the connection to a film that was targeted for little girls, except every child of that time, boy or girl, knew the theme song. Colleene's grandsons often wailed "Let it go! Let it go! It just doesn't matter anymore!" So I happened to know who the cartoon character Elsa was, and to this day it's how I remember the woman who helped me regain the use of my left hand. Her memory trick worked.

Elsa's first job was to evaluate me. She tested me with a variety of creative tasks. I squeezed a grip strength measuring device and extended my arm in all directions as she took assessments. If there had been any lingering doubt about how badly the stroke had affected my left arm, those tests removed it. I could hardly grip or hold anything at all, and my arm's range of motion was terrible. It was discouraging to see actual measurements of how pathetic I was. But it was encouraging to realize we had found the right therapy option. Elsa clearly knew what she was doing. She was both firm and sympathetic, business-like and pleasant. She would push and prod me but not torture me in the process.

She placed a small pegboard on a table in front of me. Attached to the board was a dish containing nine pegs, each about two inches long. The board had nine holes matching the diameters of the pegs. My task was to pick up the pegs and insert them into the holes with my left hand while she timed me. I could not use my right hand to help.

It took me a minute and forty seconds to get one peg into a hole. She stopped the timer and typed notes into a digital tablet. My left hand and arm were ridiculously clumsy. It was as if I were wearing a boxing glove while trying to pick up the small pegs. I could barely touch my index finger to my thumb, which made pinching a peg almost impossible. When I did manage to extract a peg from the dish, my hand strayed wildly on the way to the holes.

I immediately began to appreciate the value of an occupational therapist. Elsa knew precisely how to challenge me. Once specific weaknesses were identified, she taught me focused exercises for regaining those abilities. I diligently performed every exercise she assigned, both at the clinic with her supervision and at home on my own.

For convenience, we had scheduled the two types of therapy sessions back to back. After forty-five minutes with occupational therapist Elsa, I was introduced to Frank, the lead physical therapist. I spent several minutes explaining my painful knee to Frank, after which he started to suggest I should work through the pain, stressing the importance of regaining movement as soon as possible. I pressed my case. If Frank showed the same brutish disregard for my painful knee as Brandon had, I was going to refuse his treatment, period. I described returning to a hospital, getting x-rays, and having a doctor's confirmation that my knee was, no exaggeration, injured from repeated spasms.

To my relief, Frank took the time to examine my knee. Yep, sure enough, he could see it was badly swollen. He asked me to straighten the leg as much as I could. He did *not* grab my ankle and forcibly straighten the leg out, as Brandon had done. I showed him how little I could straighten and bend my left leg before it really started to hurt. I wasn't being a wimp, did not have a low tolerance for pain. The distress was legitimate, and it was intense. He conceded physical therapy should not cause pain. It should cause strain, not pain. Whew, I felt I could trust Frank. He wanted to push me, which is much of what physical therapists do, but he wouldn't carelessly ignore my injured knee. I could live with that.

Over the five months of therapy that were to follow, I learned to like and respect Frank a lot. I learned to like Elsa, too, and all the staff at UMC West. Thank you, Frank and Elsa, and also Bernie, Melody, and Reina. You're all credits to your profession.

As my first day of therapy wrapped up, I felt I had overcome a huge barrier. It was like starting a new job. The first day of therapy was stressful and intimidating. Everything about it caused concern – not just for me, but for Colleene, too. We had worried about simply getting me into the car at the house, then transporting me from the car into the clinic. What would the clinic look like? (It's exactly like a gym, but I didn't know that.) What would I be expected to do? Were the therapists going to be understanding and nice, like those at Providence? Or was I headed for terror and torment, as I had experienced with Brandon?

All those anxieties were quieted by the end of the day. Colleene drove me back home, and by then we were finding it easier to get me out of the car. Everything became easier as we cleared the hurdle of doing it for the first time. She rolled me into the house and down the hall to our bedroom.

It was dinner time by then. We had this down to a well-organized ritual. She brought a plate of food, already cut into bite sizes, and placed it on the tray-stand in front of the recliner. We watched some TV and went to bed early.

For the first time since the stroke, I could see a path

forming ahead of me. Dozens of concerns had been addressed, fears and anxieties were calmed. We'd worked out the right plan for my recovery and had set it in motion. There might be hope ahead after all.

7 First Stage Is The Hardest

That night (Wednesday, July 18, 2019), I went to bed feeling hopeful for the first time in two weeks. The anxieties of what to do, where to go, how to handle my stroke had been addressed. A calming sense of order settled over me.

The recliner had been wonderful for preventing spasms the night before, but it would not be comfortable to sleep in a chair two nights in a row. I wanted to sleep in bed again. Regrettably, returning to the bed meant another night of spasms, which jolted me back to reality. You may be tired of reading about my spasms by now. Believe me, I was tired of having spasms by then. The agony of spasms and spasticity would be part of my new normal for eight months. Gradually they decreased. Month four was a little less horrible than month three.

But I would have at least a few excruciating spasms every night until February of the next year.

~ ~ ~ ~

Few of us will ever know how it feels to win an Olympic Medal or a Nobel Prize. Space flight and deep-sea exploration are thrills most people will never encounter. We can watch videos of others doing those things and imagine the experiences, but only those who actually do them know how they feel.

Likewise, and fortunately, most of us will never know how it feels to have a heart attack or undergo chemotherapy – or have a stroke. Having seen people who suffered strokes, I thought I could imagine what they were going through. Having now had a stroke, it's not what I imagined at all. Several elements were complete surprises.

So many things change after a stroke, it would be tedious to list them all. Besides, every stroke is different. Many of the adjustments I had to make will not align with adjustments other stroke victims make. Still, it might help others cope if I discuss some of the conditions I was least prepared for.

Topping that list is fear. A stroke destroys basic abilities we take for granted all our lives. The sudden disabling of my left leg was surprisingly frightening. I could stand up, with considerable help, on my right leg. But my balance was shaky. My brain knew there was nothing my left leg or arm could do to stabilize me. If I lost my balance, even for a nanosecond, I would fall, and fall hard.

Not having two legs to stand on was unexpectedly

disturbing. My fundamental sense of self-reliance was altered. Every time I contemplated standing up, I had to overcome messages of terror from my brain. My mind told me not to even think about standing up. What was I, crazy? I should stay in the security of a chair or bed. I wouldn't fall down if I didn't get up.

I had to stand up eventually, of course. Overcoming the fear of falling was a learning process. I wouldn't try to stand in the middle of a room without something, or someone, to grab hold of for stability. I made sure to lock the brakes on the wheelchair before attempting to stand, and I rarely left the security of the bedroom.

Other fears crept into my thoughts. What if I couldn't make it to the toilet in time? How could I get by if something happened to Colleene? Would I spend the rest of my life being completely dependent on others? Some worries were trivial. Some were deeply frightening. Conquering fear was part of my daily routine for months after the stroke.

Next item I did not expect was pain, lots of pain. I thought a stroke meant *losing* sensation in parts of the body, not an onset of life-altering, chronic pain in the afflicted areas. Some stroke victims don't have pain, spasms, or swelling at all. I was among the unfortunate ones who had all three.

I've described the spasms. The ghastly condition of spasticity and recurring spasms will come up again several times in my story. I also experienced extreme swelling in my left hand and foot. Swelling, I now know, is common in the feet and hands of stroke victims. Our lymphatic systems remove excess fluid from our bodies through movement. When movement is paralyzed by a stroke, the lymph nodes stop pumping fluid, and it pools in the extremities. The accumulation of lymph causes swelling, then the problem amplifies itself, because the swelling further limits movement. Even if my hand had not been mostly paralyzed, the fingers were so fat I could hardly move them.

If movement reduces swelling, but the swollen limb can't move, what does one do to bring down the swelling? Jennifer and Elsa both recommended massaging and compressing the left hand. For two months, part of my daily routine was massaging my left hand with my right hand. While watching TV or listening to the radio, I'd squeeze my fingers and rub the back of my left hand, hard. I also curled the fingers of my left hand as much as I could. For hours at a time, that was my activity. I sat in a chair, straightening and curling my fingers. I could almost curl my left hand into the shape of a "C." That limited motion was enough. After a few weeks, the swelling began to subside.

As if severe spasms and swelling were not enough for me to complain about, I also experienced terrible joint pain in my left shoulder and wrist. Who knew a stroke could cause joint pain? This was not muscle pain; it was right in the joint. It hurt like hell to lift my left arm across my chest, and the pain was specific to the shoulder joint.

Fortunately, I found plenty of information about post-stroke joint pain online. A company called Saebo sells recovery aids, and their website is loaded with helpful information. Here is an excerpt about stroke-related joint pain from their site:

~ ~ ~ ~

Frozen Shoulder

Frozen shoulder is when your shoulder becomes stiff and painful to move. This is common because the muscles and ligaments surrounding the shoulder can become very weak, stiff, or even paralyzed.

Within the shoulder joint, there is a surrounding layer of tissue called a capsule. When the ligaments around the shoulder become debilitated, the patient's shoulder is strained. This strain can cause inflammation, damage, and weakness, which then causes the afflicted individual greater suffering.

Proper range of motion (ROM) exercises can prevent frozen shoulder after a stroke.

[https://www.saebo.com/blog/pain-stroke-symptoms-watch/]

~ ~ ~ ~

That helped explain it. Our muscles hold our joints together, thus disabled muscles can cause pain in joints. When certain muscles are paralyzed, the joints associated with those muscles become loose, resulting in pain.

Lifting and extending my left arm over and over became another part of my daily routine. At first, I could not straighten my left arm out in front of my body. I could get my elbow up to shoulder level, but that was as far as the arm would go.

The very first accomplishment of my recovery was, in fact, the moment I could extend my left arm out straight at shoulder level. This tiny accomplishment was so satisfying, I made a video of it. Seems silly to me now, but, at the time, it was the first indicator that I could regain functionality. Maybe I would not be an invalid the rest of my life. Recovery was possible. It was hugely encouraging.

Shoulder pain stayed with me for over a year. To this day, lifting a box or reaching for an item on an upper shelf is painful. I'll take pain over not being able to lift or reach at all, but I sure hope the irritation eventually goes away.

Pain in my wrist was also triggered by movement or strain on the joint. If my hand were resting in my lap or supported on the arm of a chair, the wrist did not hurt. Simply lifting my left arm caused instant pain in the wrist from the weight of my hand. I devised a work-around; any time I moved my left arm, I carried the afflicted left hand with my right hand. This got me through the day with less pain in my wrist.

The left hand support technique did not work at night. Sometimes I would change positions, and my left hand would flop to one side. This caused a shot of pain in the wrist that woke me up. Dammit, don't you know, this would happen just when I was enjoying a reprieve from leg spasms. I didn't know the wrist pain would last so long, so I didn't do much to address it at first. I tried to live with it by using my support-one-hand-with-the-other trick. After a month of nightly pain, we got a wrist brace and put it on at bedtime every night. That worked wonderfully. Weakness and sharp pain in the wrist lasted about three months. After that the pain diminished, but it remained pitifully weak for several more months.

Forgive me if I seem to be engaging in a self-pity party. For two months after the stroke, my daily existence amounted to contending with pain and trying to catch up on sleep. That summer is something of a blur to me now. Many hours were spent sitting in the recliner, trying to nap between spasms.

At night, I discovered the most comfortable sleeping position was on my left side, the side affected by the stroke. For some reason, the spasms occurred less often in that position. Also, I could rest my left wrist flat on the bed. Trouble was, rolling onto my left side required tremendous effort. Sometimes it took half a dozen attempts, rocking side to side on my back, to gain enough momentum to shift my bulk onto my side. Changing positions in bed is crazy difficult when one side of the body is paralyzed.

Signs Of Hope

Those long days and nights of pain would have been unbearable, had there not been days of improvement to lift my spirits. The first milestone was being able to extend my arm, as mentioned previously. That development occurred on Thursday, July 18, almost three weeks after the stroke. Simply stretching out my left arm, as one would do to turn on a lamp, was monumental to my state of mind. Regaining that little motion emboldened my confidence that I could regain every other lost ability.

It did not happen by itself. After my first visit with the good therapists at UMC West, when my path to recovery became visible, I focused on the two main principles of improvement: regular exercise and unflappable faith. Those two principles could be the essence of all achievements. If we believe in ourselves, and we're willing to work, it's amazing what we can accomplish.

Therapy showed me how exercise leads to recovery. It's like learning to play a musical instrument or use computer software. The brain picks up every skill through repetition, and each ability builds on previous skills.

With that concept in mind, the way I reached the first milestone with my left arm was to start simple. Since I couldn't extend my arm out in front of myself, I started with numerous repetitions of exercises my arm *could* do. Sitting upright in my wheelchair, I let my arm hang down at my side, then lifted it over my lap. That was it. That was all I could do. I was not holding a weight or adding resistance in any way. Lifting my arm from my side to above my knee was the beginning of it all. I did that tiny motion twenty reps at a time, five times a day, for a total of one hundred repetitions a day.

I learned the brain has a remarkable ability to mirror the two sides of the body. If a person lifts weights with only one arm, the other arm develops some muscle mass to mirror the arm that's doing the lifting. This is a process of the brain, not the muscles themselves. I learned about this phenomenon from internet research, which I did a lot in the early stage of recovery. Studying stroke recovery was one way I passed long days of boredom.

When I did my simple side-to-lap movements with my left arm, I matched the motion with my right arm. That way, I hoped, the brain was re-learning to control my afflicted arm by mirroring the motion in my good arm.

After every round of twenty reps, I tried the motion I was working for – extending my arm in front of myself. No progress was detectable for the first week. Then I started reaching further and further out after each round. Finally, almost three weeks after the stroke, I did it. Like a mummy from an old movie, I stretched both arms straight forward, left arm parallel to right. Then I didn't want to stop doing it! I continued my reps, only now I brought both arms up from my sides to full extension in front of myself. Often, I couldn't resist calling attention to my feat. "Watch this!" I'd say to Colleene, as I held out my left arm. Such a simple movement was a huge accomplishment to me at the time.

Once I proved to myself I could lift my arm up to shoulder level, the next goal was lifting my arm over my head. Using the same technique of mirroring the movement, I raised both arms to shoulder level over and over. Each time I pushed the left arm to go as high as it could. Day by day, this repetition worked. I could feel my arm rebuilding strength and range of motion. One week after the achievement of lifting my arm to shoulder level, I managed to raise my left arm above my head. I could signal a touchdown if I were a football referee. It's something every school child does in class, yet raising my hand above my head seemed a giant milestone. This was proof that, with time and effort, I could become a functioning human again.

Have you ever watched a movie or TV show that depicts a person recovering from a neural injury and wondered how accurate it is? In a heart-stopping episode of the series *Breaking Bad*, DEA Agent Hank is shot by the evil Salamanca Brothers, and the bullet pierces his spine. This leaves his lower body paralyzed. In several ensuing episodes, we see Hank exerting monumental effort to take a few steps in physical therapy. A harness holds him up, so he's hardly putting any weight on his legs, yet each tiny step seems an enormous struggle. I'm a fan of the *Breaking Bad* series, but I wondered if that depiction of Hank's recovery was true to life. He appeared to be trying to drag a truck uphill. When he managed to move one foot a few inches, his therapists cheered it as a major accomplishment.

I would have liked to live out the rest of my life without learning this for myself, but I now know recovering from neuron damage is exactly as *Breaking Bad* depicted it. Four weeks after a stroke, lifting my left arm above my head felt as if I were hoisting a fifty-pound weight. It required tremendous effort. My arm was exhausted after doing it only three times. Regaining the slightest strength took months of repetition. For reasons I do not understand, the brain interprets loss of control as loss of strength. Muscles do atrophy somewhat after a stroke from lack of use. But the muscles in my left arm seemed nonexistent after only two weeks. The dramatic loss of strength happened in my brain. It was not muscle weakness.

I suppose the brain reacts to losing command of muscles the same as we do when a TV remote control battery goes dead. What's the first thing we do when the "clicker" doesn't work? We click harder! We wave the remote around, hold it over our heads, and bang it on the coffee table while pressing the buttons over and over. The TV still works fine. The remote still works fine, too, but a piece is missing.

Difference between a brain and a remote control is: a brain needs years of work to fix missing pieces. Replacing batteries in a remote control takes thirty seconds.

My arm exercises were only part of my therapy, of course. Each week I had two sessions of physical and occupational therapy. We scheduled these back-to-back, so the four sessions could be done with two trips to the UMC clinic. Frank and Elsa and the staff started me out on very minimal exercises, but they quickly increased expectations. A major part of a therapist's job is pushing patients to do more, always pressing us beyond our comfort zones.

Much of what we did in the beginning was stretching. Stretching muscles, I learned, is almost as beneficial as flexing them for recovering neurological control. I was in a wheelchair until mid-September, so the types of leg exercises I could do were limited. I spent a lot of time on stationary machines. They'd roll me to a machine, help me out of the wheelchair and onto the machine, then leave me to pedal away for ten minutes.

Exercise, rest, and pain occupied much of my time for the first two months of recovery. Spasms interfered with my sleep almost every night, so I took a lot of naps during the day. I understand how people can become addicted to pain medications. I never took anything stronger than gabapentin or ibuprofen, but some days I had to stop myself from swallowing dozens of those pills.

Simple activities demand vastly more time when only half the body is operational. Getting out of bed, getting dressed, and having breakfast filled up the first hour and a half of each morning. Bodily functions don't cease after a stroke, but performing bodily functions changes dramatically. A bowel movement could take an hour. I didn't mind. Sitting on a toilet, waiting for my colon to do its thing, was preferable to using a potty chair or bedpan. Besides, I had nothing else to do.

Colleene was essential to everything I did, which meant the excessive time I needed for simple tasks was time taken away from her days, too. We were fortunate she had started working from home a year earlier. She does medical billing. When we moved from Reno to El Paso, the company she worked for didn't want to lose her. She was their senior billing agent, having been at that job eighteen years, so they set her up to continue doing the job remotely.

Her years as a steadfast, reliable employee paid off. Colleene's employers were very accommodating with her schedule to allow her to attend to me. Before my stroke, she usually worked from 7:00 AM to 3:00 PM. For the first stage of my recovery, she continued to log on at 7:00. Then she'd log off at 9:30 to help me start my day.

Our morning ritual started with merely pulling me up to a sitting position in bed. That alone was so much work we both needed a few minutes to recuperate before proceeding. Dressing me was like putting clothes on a mannequin. My job was to sit still as garments were manipulated onto my frame. One of us had to lift my left hand and point it into the appropriate shirt sleeve. I could elevate my left foot just enough for her to slip on a pair of shorts.

Once I was dressed, Colleene planted herself in front of me and helped me stand up on my right leg. Then I did my shuffle-step on one foot to the recliner. Lastly, she brought breakfast and my morning battery of pills before she logged back in to work. This was our morning routine for all of July and August of 2019.

My activity level dropped to practically nothing. I could have put on several pounds during that time, except my food intake also dropped significantly. On many days, I was wrestling with so much pain I simply didn't feel like eating. On days when the pain wasn't so bad, I was tempted to indulge in boredom eating, except I was extremely motivated to become healthier. Two years earlier, mindless snacking would have been my way of comforting myself. A big plate of nachos, a ham sandwich, a bowl of ice cream with half a dozen Oreo cookies – such delights had been my go-to pleasures to combat boredom for years. Those "delights" likely contributed to my stroke.

I had committed to losing weight several months before the stroke. The key to weight loss, I've learned, is resolve. I'd say that's the key to any achievement. I can't pinpoint what prompted my resolve, but in January of 2019, I became doggedly determined to get healthy again. It's incredible the stroke happened a few months after I started taking better care of myself than I had in years. I lost almost twenty pounds in the six months prior to the stroke. After the stroke, my resolve deepened. I'd lost twenty more pounds by the end of August, two months after the stroke. Few things are as motivating as a major health issue.

Showering was impossible for the first two months. I was dependent on Colleene to maintain reasonable cleanliness. Twice a week she gave me a sponge bath. With all her might, she'd roll me onto my side and spread a thick towel behind me on the bed. Then she'd roll me onto the other side and lay down another towel. She rubbed me down with a washcloth from a bucket of warm water and a little bath oil. No need to towel dry afterward. This was El Paso. My skin air-dried in about two minutes, and the cooling effect felt nice.

Washing my hair was something I could do myself,

quite satisfactorily, with a technique suggested by Jennifer while I was in the hospital. She demonstrated how I could roll my wheelchair up to the edge of a kitchen sink, grip the counter with my right hand and pull myself to a standing position, then lean against the counter for stability while I shampooed my head over the sink. First time I tried that was scary as hell. The standing up part was easy. But bending over the sink while running water on my head caused dizziness. Often I had to stop shampooing and lean heavily on the counter for a few moments to get my balance. Colleene and Brian stood on either side of me in case I started to tip over. I never became unsteady enough to think I would fall, and the wheelchair was right behind me, but it was reassuring to have them there.

Overcoming the fear of falling took months. Even now, after more than a year of recovery, I still have fleeting moments of panic when stepping off a curb or turning around too quickly. Brain damage is no fun, no fun at all.

8 Settling In For The New Normal

Around the third week of August, I began to have days when I wasn't exhausted or contending with spasms all day. By then I had grown accustomed to having one side of my body mostly paralyzed. I had learned to perform many tasks one-handed. There were some things, such as squeezing toothpaste onto a toothbrush, that I never found ways to do with one hand. Other things, such as operating a computer, I became rather adept at doing single-handed. Colleene and I learned what I could do for myself and what she had to help me with, and we developed methods for all my daily tasks. My day-to-day life as a partially paralyzed person became routine.

Mid August was also when I began to regain basic functions. Among the most important was I could stand up and take a few steps on my own. That meant I no longer needed Colleene to help me use the toilet. What a relief for both of us. Few things are more humiliating than needing help to get on and off a commode.

I had been released from Providence Hospital six weeks earlier, so the time had come for my first follow-up appointment with a general practitioner. Colleene drove me to see Dr. Alonzo at UMC West. This would be a wonderful day of good news.

Everything – all my indicators – had improved since I left the hospital. My blood pressure had dropped from 130/87 to 112/68. Sodium was down, cholesterol was down, and, sweetest news anyone wants to hear, I had lost twenty pounds. The doctor's assessment was also quite positive. He was impressed I could already stand and walk a few steps.

Of all the physicians and therapists I'd consulted, Dr. Alonzo was the first medical professional who seemed to understand the spasms I was suffering, and he offered a homespun remedy – mustard. It had no medical studies backing it up, but he had heard mustard sometimes helps relieve spasms. That very evening, Ritz Crackers with dollops of mustard became part of my dinner. Whether it helped or not is hard to say. The spasms did not abruptly cease after I started consuming mustard, but they did *seem* to be less severe.

We came home from that doctor visit with a refreshing attitude of renewed confidence. I was doing it; I was recovering. In fact, I was considerably healthier than before I had the stroke! I mean, aside from being partially paralyzed, my health indicators had all improved.

The next step to work on was walking. Late one afternoon, after Colleene had logged off from work, I asked her to roll me out to the living room. One of her grandsons brought out my walker and set it in front of me. Then, once I stood up, the grandson's job was to follow me with the wheelchair, keeping it about a foot behind me. This way, if I started to fall, I could simply drop into the chair. The grandsons took turns doing this. It was a fun game to them.

I managed twenty steps the first time. It felt wonderful, although the exertion was surprisingly taxing. I had to lean hard on the walker. Walking was not as strenuous for me as it was for Hank in *Breaking Bad*, but twenty steps took a lot out of me. When I reached the kitchen, I collapsed into the wheelchair, done for the day. Three days later I managed thirty steps. Within a few more days I could do thirty steps down the hall and back, for a total of sixty strides. I was dependent on the walker, and lifting my left foot for each step required considerable effort, but I was walking, doggone it.

By the end of August, I quit using the wheelchair altogether around the house. I still needed the walker, but I could move about the house without needing someone to push me in a wheelchair.

On Saturday, August 24, I took my first shower since the stroke. That was eight weeks to the day since the last time I stood under running water – longest I've ever gone without a bath or shower in my life. It was wonderful.

This monumental accomplishment – yes, taking that shower seemed monumental – was only possible by a happenchance of our shower's design. The bathroom by the "Grandma Room" of Colleene's house has a stand-up shower stall, not a bathtub/shower combo. A person stepped down into the shower. If I had needed to step over the side of a tub, it likely would have been another month before I could take a shower. With the step-down shower, I could place the walker firmly on the floor of the shower stall, then use it to steady myself as I stepped in. Once in the stall, there was a ledge I could sit down on – another lucky design element that made showering possible.

There are so many simple tasks we take for granted, until we can't do them: taking a shower, using a toilet, putting on a shirt, getting a drink of water from the kitchen. Being able to do those tasks made me start to feel normal again, independent again. I never knew pouring my own coffee could be so satisfying.

The only thing that was slow to show progress was my left hand. Elsa told me that was normal. In her experience as an occupational therapist, hands are the last part of the body to recover. Humans have the most sophisticated hands of all animals. That sophistication is not actually in the hands; it's in our brains. The region of a human brain that controls hands is second in size only to the area devoted to eyes.

Nonetheless, my left hand stunned me one day with a big leap of improvement. On Sunday, August 25, the day after my invigorating first shower, I woke up to a new sensation in my hand. My left hand felt more present than it had the day before. I was more aware of my fingers, if that makes sense. For eight weeks, I had not been able to touch my thumb with my fingers. I could hardly curl my fingers to make the shape of a "C" with my hand, and moving my wrist continued to be quite painful.

That Sunday morning, my hand felt awake. Without even sitting up, I decided to give it a try. One, two, three – just like that, I touched my first three fingers to my thumb. I couldn't quite get the pinky finger to make the reach, but the index, middle, and ring fingers easily contacted the tip of my thumb.

"Wow, welcome back!" I said out loud to my left hand. I could hardly wait to show Colleene. When she came back to the room to begin our morning routine, I had put on my shirt and shorts and was sitting up in bed – first time I had done those things without her help since the stroke. I held up my left hand and proudly demonstrated my finger-to-thumb touch ability. I'm sure she felt as parents do when their children proudly demonstrate trivial abilities. Nonetheless, as parents do for their children, she exuded praise and admiration, as if she'd never seen a person do that before.

My coffee tasted a little better that morning. I still couldn't hold a coffee cup with my left hand, but, as of that day, my confidence grew that my left hand *would* be useful again, perhaps soon.

~ ~ ~ ~

By the end of August, pain and spasms did not absorb so much of my time. Simple tasks, such as getting dressed, combing my hair, and going to the bathroom, no longer took hours out of each day. I began to need ways to occupy myself. A few centuries ago, the only productive things I might have been able to do were churn butter and sort beans. Thanks to modern technology, I got a job!

It was not a great job, and, even at that, it was terribly difficult to find. Working from home is the dream of hordes of people, disabled or not, and that has caused hordes of scammers to pop up with fake work-from-home schemes. A person who truly wants a telecommute gig has to spend hours sifting out the scumbags. It's sad how many swindlers use the internet to prey on well-intended folks. Here's a tip I learned right away: If a work-from-home opportunity requires you to send *them* money first, for registration or a processing fee or some other nonsense, it's a scam.

It's also disappointing how many companies are not tapping into the benefits of telecommuters. That may change soon, especially after the onerous coronavirus of 2020, but in the fall of 2019, decent work-from-home gigs were hard to find.

The job I landed was writing articles for a web page content provider. One of the ways web sites improve search engine rankings is through continually posting fresh content. Where there is a need, free enterprise finds a way. Website services have sprung up that hire writers to offer steady supplies of fresh content. Writing content and designing software are among the few jobs commonly farmed out to freelance telecommuters, from what I observed.

The company that hired me focused on cosmetic surgery clinics. I researched and wrote dozens of articles about laser hair removal, tummy-tucks, skin rejuvenation, and, yes, breast enhancements. I was paid by the article, not by the hour, which I preferred. I had to work the keyboard with only my right hand, so typing took longer than usual. To keep my left hand engaged, I'd use my left index finger to press the "Shift" key whenever a capital letter was needed. That's as much as my left hand could do. I became quite adept at my one-handed typing technique, but, naturally, it was significantly slower than using both hands. With my slow typing and the extensive research some articles required, I ended up making less than minimum wage most days. Regardless, it was gratifying to find a way to earn an income from home while recovering from a stroke. Writing articles for other people's websites prompted the prospect of writing and marketing my own material, and thus the idea of this book was born.

When I simply could not find the motivation to write another article about hair removal or sagging arm skin, I whiled away my time doing other stuff on the computer, as so many of us do these days. I'm not into social media – not that I object to it or think less of folks who enjoy socializing digitally; it's just not my thing. My preferred way of wasting time on the internet is gaming and watching videos.

Time spent on those frivolous pursuits was not entirely wasted. Most of the videos I watched were educational; I learned a ton about stroke recovery and self-publishing, which was useful in writing this book. Playing computer games was – and I'm not altogether joking about this – therapy! My left hand could not press buttons on the keyboard, but, with effort, I taught myself to play World of Warcraft with my left hand on the mouse and right hand on the keyboard, the reverse of normal. Because it required extra effort and concentration, using my left hand on the mouse was therapy. Elsa said so. It was challenging and frustrating at first. My game characters died many ignoble deaths. But working the mouse with my left hand became easier each time I played. Therefore, I hold fast to my contention that playing computer games was therapy.

Without knowing it at the time, finding activities to do was good for me in ways beyond physical therapy. Having something productive to do and something fun to do are essential to every person's mental well being. We can only be idle for so long. Our minds need to engage, to be active. Being passively entertained is different from doing an entertaining activity. Reading, watching videos, listening to music – those are all good for occupying our time. But anyone recovering from a debilitating condition benefits from finding pursuits that require active participation.

Further, I contend that doing productive activities is fundamental to a healthy human experience. Yes, I know, there are people who seem not to be afflicted with a desire to feel useful. Whether disabled or not, there are some who are content to live entirely off the fruits of other people's labor. I feel sorry for such folks. Doing something productive makes us feel valued, that we are contributing something to the universe. Having a job means a person is participating with the community at large. We engage with society by performing services for each other. Feeling productive, earning one's own way (whether it's for a paycheck or as a contributing family member), doing for others to balance what others do for us, brings an important factor to a fulfilling life.

I realize I was lucky. Not everyone can find a paying job while recovering from a stroke. That's okay. There are loads of things people can do to give themselves a sense of purpose. Being productive doesn't necessarily mean being paid to do something. Volunteer work contributes to the greater good. Even if it's joining a political campaign or volunteering for a historical society, I believe any person in recovery benefits from finding productive endeavors. It did wonders for my state of mind.

All of us need to do fun things, too. We need activities that require engagement. A person who isn't into computer games could do crossword puzzles, play backgammon with someone they like, take up a hobby, learn a new craft. Our state of being is profoundly impacted by our state of doing.

9 Two Steps Forward, One Step Back

Here's a mind-blower I stumbled onto while researching our learned abilities: Doctors believe a newborn baby sees everything upside down and backward for the first few hours, perhaps days, of its life. As you likely know, the lenses of our eyes invert images onto our retinas. To demonstrate this, try holding a magnifying glass out at arm's length. Everything you see through the glass will be inverted. Our eyes send upside down and backward views of the world to our optic nerves. Our brains constantly turn images back right side up, allowing us to use our vision to function. That's fascinating, but more amazing is this ability is something our brains have to *learn*.

We can't remember the first couple of years of our lives, so we don't have a reference for how we felt as we learned to walk, hold objects, recognize danger, and speak our native languages. We have to observe babies to see how we humans struggle to learn basic abilities. The average baby takes its first step at around twelve months old – a full year into its life. It's another full year before a baby can run, but we all know a toddler's run is pure folly. They tramp their feet awkwardly and fall frequently. We humans don't run full stride with power and agility until at least age five. Stepping up and down stairs, throwing, catching, climbing, dancing; everything we do is learned.

A stroke wipes out big chunks of that learning. Like erasing a partition from a hard drive, a stroke deletes entire portions of our functionality. The muscles are still intact, but we can't use them. Controlling the muscles has to be relearned. When we stroke victims understand this and come to terms with it, the lengthy path to recovery seems more tolerable. Or perhaps I should say it seems less *in*tolerable.

Truth is, it stinks. In an instant, abilities our brains spent years learning are gone, wiped out, destroyed. I know how lucky I was. My stroke was nowhere near as serious as what many others suffer, and I had tremendous support throughout my recovery. Some days, it was joyful to sense my progress. Other days, I felt crushing despair over abilities I'd been robbed of. It's terribly frustrating to be incapacitated.

~ ~ ~ ~

The last day of August is my birthday. My Uncle Jim and his wife, Diane, drove down from Albuquerque that weekend. My birthday was coincidental to their visit, but it gave us something to celebrate.

Colleene and I met Jim and Diane at a local

restaurant. This was a big deal for me. It was my first pleasure outing since the stroke. For all of July and August, the only times I left the house were for physical therapy or a doctor visit.

I could get into and out of a car on my own by the end of August, yet I was not fully comfortable walking, even with the walker. Colleene worried there would be tricky walkways or other obstacles that could cause me to fall. I was eager to show off my progress, but I relented to Colleene's concerns. We took the wheelchair with us to the restaurant. Colleene loaded that damned wheelchair into and out of my SUV dozens of times in the summer of 2019.

I'd never been rolled through a restaurant in a wheelchair. It's weird to glide past other patrons at eye level. The wheelchair was the right decision. It would have been challenging to plod my way through the restaurant with the walker. I was able to stand up from the wheelchair and transfer into a booth, which was a relief. I didn't like the idea of sitting awkwardly at a table with my bulky wheelchair taking up part of an aisle.

A birthday dinner at a restaurant was wonderfully satisfying. The entire process rejuvenated my sense of self. I took a shower that morning, something I couldn't do until just six days earlier, and dressed myself in real clothes, not the knock-around house clothes of a disabled person. I made myself presentable and went out among people. It was as close as I'd felt to normal in two months. Stroke recovery has highs and lows. August ended on a high.

Physical therapist Frank did an evaluation of my

progress in early September. This is significant. Therapists have specific techniques to gauge a person's progress. Elsa said I was not ready for evaluation from her yet. Physical therapy focuses on walking, balance, and leg strength – Frank's territory. Occupational therapy is for arm strength and hand dexterity – Elsa's territory. My hand and arm were improving slower than my leg, so Elsa's evaluation would come later.

Frank put me through a variety of range of motion measurements, strength and balance tests, and he typed results into a tablet. He congratulated me with high marks for my progress. Then he raised his expectations way beyond my comfort zone. Frank told me I should be walking again within six weeks. No wheelchair, no walker, not even a cane; he wanted my goal to be walking unaided by mid-October.

Wow! The hospital had prepared me to think it might be a year before I could walk at all, and Frank wants me hoofing around autonomously in half that time. It was encouraging to think my recovery could accelerate so much. On the other hand, I was still unsteady as hell on my feet. Simply standing up was frightening. The thought of walking so soon without any stabilizing device made me uneasy. As I have mentioned, Frank liked to push expectations.

Thing was, I realized he may have been right. At the clinic, Frank and Bernie would flank me on strolls across the room, and sometimes they pulled the walker away. Although I felt unsteady, I never started to fall. The guys walked with me for security only. They never had to physically hold me up. Perhaps I could be walking by the end of October. I was sure going to try.

Then the spasms came back. Those horrific leg contractions had been declining at the end of August. My sprained knee had begun to heal. The swelling had diminished. Putting weight on that leg caused only minor pain. After two months of merciless nightly spasms that perpetually re-injured my knee, I thought the nightmare was ending.

The horror resumed Friday evening, September 6. I was sitting in the recliner watching TV after dinner. Suddenly, as if a high voltage wire touched my leg, my hamstring jerked so hard it almost knocked me out of the chair. The spasm lasted several seconds, during which I bellowed a string of curses, and then it was done. Half a minute later, another jolt of electricity shot through the back of my leg. Then another one fifteen seconds later. That was three wrenching spasms in a span of two minutes.

I tried to settle down in the chair, breathing heavily and not knowing if more cramps were on the way. I looked at Colleene and said, "Not this again."

Yes, it turned out, that again. After we went to bed, I had a fourth spasm, then a fifth. If this was to be another night of agony-by-spasms, I decided to count them. By 4:00 AM, the spasm tally was up to thirty-eight. Ever had thirty-eight charley horses in one night? I don't recommend it. Then, as had often happened before, the spasms relented, allowing me to sleep soundly the last few hours of the night.

Next morning, I was not surprised to discover my

knee was swollen up again to double its normal size. Bending that knee or putting weight on it caused familiar knife-stabs of pain. The spasms had returned. All the remedies I tried – mustard, magnesium, ibuprofen, Absorbine Jr. – were not enough to calm the errant signals from my brain.

I had several more terrible nights. Four days after Frank told me I might be walking again in six weeks, I had to halt much of my physical therapy. The knee would hardly allow me to stand up, much less walk. Frank liked to push me, but he was not a heartless tormentor. At my next physical therapy session, he took one look at the swollen knee, shook his head and said, "It's okay. We can work on other things for a while. When that knee gets better, we'll try walking again."

The return of spasms had a troubling effect on me. My perception of reality started to skew again. I began to doubt myself, to question if I could take any more of this. I started saying a little prayer after each crushing cramp. "Please, if someone can hear me, let that be the last one. I can't go on living like this." If anyone was listening, apparently they wanted to prove I could go on living like that – the spasms kept coming. Sometimes I would hit my leg with my fist, hard, to distract from the torture in my hamstring. Each agonizing spasm raised the bar of pain I could tolerate.

The bar can only go so high. Each of us has a limit to how much pain we can endure, and I reached mine. The brain does something remarkable when pain exceeds the maximum it can stand. It numbs itself. At one point, I became strangely detached. The spasms put me into some kind of trance state, like an out-of-body experience. They still hurt, but somehow I was removed from the pain.

With my re-injured knee, several weeks passed before I could put the slightest weight on my left leg again. No way I'd meet Frank's ambitious goal of walking unaided by the end of October. That was a discouraging set-back, but, overall, I was making progress. Two steps forward, one step back still results in one step forward.

That was the status of my left leg in early September. A little later in the month, my left hand started to show noticeable progress. It was wonderful to open jars and turn doorknobs with my left hand again.

The progress in my left hand was noticed by occupational therapist Elsa. My first evaluation with her took place in mid-September. As Frank had done two weeks earlier, Elsa awarded me top marks for gains in strength, dexterity, and range of motion.

Remember the pegboard test I took on my first day of therapy? It took me a minute and forty seconds to get a single peg into a hole on that first attempt. Elsa brought the pegboard back out for my re-evaluation. This time, I got all nine pegs into their holes and back out again, but it took me over two minutes. I thought that was pretty great. Then Elsa had me do the task right-handed. With my good hand, I could get all the pegs in and out of the holes in under thirty seconds. Yep, still had work to do with my left hand. Therapists Elsa and Frank both demonstrated time and again how well they understood their professions. Elsa knew that having me perform the pegboard test with my right hand would perfectly demonstrate how much rehabilitation my left hand still needed.

After congratulating me on my progress, Elsa asked if there were specific things I wanted to work on. What activities were missing from my previous life that I wanted to get back? That was easy to answer; I wished I could use my left hand to type again. I'd become pretty fast at typing one-handed, but, obviously, I'd do much better if my left hand could perform its part.

Elsa asked if I had tried typing left-handed recently. Well, no, actually, I hadn't. "Try it," she said. "You might be surprised."

The next day was Friday The 13th. I mention that simply to establish the date, not to suggest something dreadful was about to happen. It turned out to be a benchmark day of ups and downs. Colleene and I did our usual morning routine. Mornings in West Texas were becoming tolerably cool, so we enjoyed our first cups of coffee out on the patio. I was using the wheelchair to get around again, thanks to my spasms-induced sprained knee. Colleene would roll me to the back door, then I'd use the walker to hobble the few steps to a patio chair.

After breakfast, Colleene parked me at my desk. I was hopeful, but also realistic. Last time I tried to work a keyboard with my left hand, it felt like typing while wearing a baseball mitt. This time, my fingers found their buttons and pressed them on cue. My left hand could type! I sent e-mails to several friends, making sure they knew every Q-W-E-R-T had been appropriately typed by the left hand. It was glorious. I felt as if I had found a long lost friend.

Later that evening, relishing the development of my left hand, I tried to shake pepper left-handed onto my cauliflower at dinner. I could not do it. I could pick up the pepper shaker and hold it over my plate with my left hand – abilities that took two months to relearn after the stroke – but I could not will my arm to make the simple back-and-forth movement to shake out pepper.

I was furious with disappointment. How could this be? I could type with my left hand, but I couldn't jiggle a stupid pepper shaker? I'm grateful that I kept my composure. I wanted to scream obscenities and hurl the pepper shaker against a wall, but that would not have accomplished anything. My frustration was with myself, not with anyone else at the dinner table. I needed to get a handle on my emotional incontinence.

Moments of despondency are common among stroke victims. My old friend Gina told me of someone she knew who, after a stroke, would sometimes pick up her limp hand with her strong hand and throw it roughly to her side. I understand such outbursts of frustration. My stroke was relatively mild, yet I often struggled with angry outbursts over my condition. I can only imagine the aggravation some victims feel whose strokes are more serious than mine. Some struggle with crippling spasticity for more than a decade after a stroke. Others never regain their ability to speak or walk or type. My heart goes out to such people. A stroke can devastate a person's life.

The good news is most stroke sufferers can reclaim much of what strokes took from them. It isn't easy. There are moments when we feel disheartened or angry about our frailties. Physical therapy can be unpleasant and slow to show results. A lengthy recovery challenges our will and clouds our belief. There will be bad days, understandably, but I believe a person who maintains an overall positive attitude and puts in the necessary effort will enjoy significant improvement over time. Hang in there, and don't give up. It will get better.

Being unable to dispense pepper from a shaker caused one of my moments of despondency, only a few hours after I'd felt downright giddy over typing with my left hand. The disability had caught me by surprise. I had no idea shaking my hand back and forth required so much brain power.

At dinner the next evening, my mind was better prepared to contend with my weakness. I deliberately picked up the pepper shaker with my left hand and slowly rocked it back and forth. It took so long to get pepper out, my arm became tired, and I had to rest it for a minute. When I resumed my attempt, others at the table offered to do it for me. They meant well, but shaking pepper for me was the opposite of helping me. I needed to do this, partly to retrain my brain to jostle my hand back and forth, and partly to rebuild my confidence. I could have switched hands and shaken that pepper container vigorously with my right arm. That would have got the job done, but it would not have benefited my afflicted hand. It's now many months later, and I still cannot shake a pepper container as briskly as I'd like with my left hand. I have to remind myself that being able to shake it at all is progress.

Frustrating as it was, I forced myself to use my left

hand for as many things as I could. I have to credit Elsa for making me consciously use my left hand whenever possible. One day at the UMC clinic, I was taking a break from physical therapy and having a cup of water. Elsa saw me holding the cup in my right hand and scolded me, teasingly, but her message stuck; using the damaged hand to do anything, even to hold a cup of water, is therapy.

The wildly fluctuating highs and lows of recovery began to level out in mid-October. Therapy moved into what I think of as the second stage. The first stage was getting my left hand and leg to wake up and work at all. Second stage was progressing to what I call functionality; being able to perform useful movements. I'd liken it to learning how to roller skate. First stage is simply being able to stand up with wheels under our feet. Second stage is learning how to function, to roll without falling. Third stage is building the confidence to have fun with this ability.

Throwing a weighted ball was among my favorite triumphs. In the first weeks after the stroke, I could not pick up a pencil with my left hand. By September, I could open and close my fingers and grasp small objects, but I could not hold the two-kilogram ball Melody offered me one day at therapy. A couple of weeks later, at my therapy session of September 30, I could not only hold that weighted ball in my left hand, I could throw it.

This was one thing we did in therapy that was actually fun. The clinic had a small trampoline set up at a slight incline. That gave me a target to throw the weighted ball against, and it bounced back to me. I threw and caught the ball with my left hand. Throwing and catching seem such simple activities. Having a stroke makes a person appreciate how much brain power it takes to clutch an item, propel it at a target with precise force and trajectory, release it at exactly the right moment, then follow it with the eyes, judge distance and speed, and catch it. Doing all that with a ball I previously could not even pick up was exhilarating.

Think of a toddler again. Throw a nerf ball at a one-year-old, and it will bounce off their head, usually prompting giggles and claps. The little tike is amazed you could throw something. We adults think nothing of wadding a sandwich wrapper and tossing it into a trash can. We forget it took our brains years to learn so much coordination.

Throwing and catching a ball are excellent therapy, and they're fun activities. It became a favorite pastime to toss a football in the backyard with one of Colleene's grandsons. I made all my throws left-handed, so we couldn't stand more than about fifteen feet apart. I scored bonus points when I made a catch left-handed.

The first few times we tossed the football, I stood with the walker nearby for stability. Every left-handed throw tested my balance. Think of trying to throw something after spinning in place ten times. There were several occasions when I thought for sure I would fall. It upset Colleene to see me grab the walker to steady myself. The risk of a fall was real. A pang of fear shot through me with every left-handed throw. But I knew regaining stability required pushing myself out of my comfort zone.

Autumn is my favorite season, partly because it marks the end of scorching hot weather in West Texas, and partly because it's football season. I'm not one of those obnoxious guys who lives and breathes sports, but I do enjoy football on TV. In the fall of 2019, it was particularly pleasant to be able to watch football from the couch. I could not sit on something so low as a couch for the first three months after the stroke. Sitting – and, more important, standing back up – from the couch required more strength and coordination than I could exert. Thus, merely sitting on the couch again seemed an accomplishment.

Other simple tasks became available to me in the fall of 2019. I could walk into the kitchen, pour my own coffee, and even make my own breakfast. I could turn on a lamp left-handed, carry out the trash, pull on socks (try doing that one-handed!), and turn a doorknob.

Having progressed to what I called stage two, I felt ready to advance my level of therapy at home. Up to that point, my home exercises had been limited to very simple movements – curling my fingers, holding small objects, lifting my arm to shoulder level, standing up, wiggling my toes. In mid-October, I began pushing myself to more rigorous workouts.

It's comical now to remember what I did in my first exercise sessions. Standing was still difficult, so I lifted weights while sitting in a chair. For my left arm, "lifting weights" meant hoisting Colleene's two-pound pink dumbbell, and even that was too much to lift over my head. How many times have you lifted a gallon jug of milk or juice out of your fridge? My left arm struggled to lift a quarter that weight. It would be December before I could heave a five-pound weight above my head with my left arm.

I did crunches on the bed. At the time, this was hugely satisfying, because simply sitting up in bed had been impossible for several weeks. Being able to sit upright, lean back, then bring my upper body back upright on the bed felt wonderful.

While still on the bed, I rolled over and did leg curls from a face-down position. Often I put on ankle weights to add mild resistance. Like every exercise I did then, this was invigorating for both body and mind. The hamstring muscle of my left leg was one of the body parts most impacted by my stroke. That's where the painfully forceful spasms usually attacked. Strangely, when I flexed the hamstring consciously, it was limp and uncooperative. Uncontrolled contractions were severe; controlled contractions were feeble. This is the nature of brain damage. I could feel the back of my left leg respond to the leg curls. Doing that silly movement over and over was instrumental, I think, in overcoming the spasms.

Other exercises I did at that time would remind you of an aerobics class at an old-folks home. I did toe extensions against the floor from a sitting position. That pitiful little motion demanded significant exertion for my left calf muscle. How pathetically weak I was. My workouts included standing up, briefly, and making half-circle motions with my left leg while steadying myself on the walker. I'd point my foot out to the front, then draw it around the side and point it out behind myself, then bring it back around to the front. I barely managed two minutes of that minimal movement before I needed to sit back down and rest.

Compared to what a strong, healthy person could do, my little workouts seemed hardly worth the effort. Pointing the toe of my left foot, lifting a two-pound weight with my left hand – these tiny actions were a surprising amount of work with no discernible reward. Seeing results took a discouraging length of time, but the effort paid off. Little by little, I regained both muscle mass and brain connectivity. By Halloween, I stopped needing the wheelchair altogether.

I again have to give credit to my therapist for spurring my development. Frank relentlessly prodded me to get out of the wheelchair. Being without the security of my chair was unnerving at first. But Frank was right; pressing myself past the fear was an enormous confidence builder.

The fear was not from concern my left leg would buckle. The leg had regained most of its sturdiness by the end of October. The fear was from lack of stability. Walking is more than supporting our bodies with our legs; it's *balancing* our bodies on our legs. For several weeks, every time I stepped from my right foot to my left, I felt compelled to grab hold of something. I had never appreciated the brain power needed for something so simple as balance.

Halloween Night amplified my new appreciation for balance. It was our first Halloween in the new house. I was pleased to see how many folks in the neighborhood participated in decorating their houses and how many trick-or-treating kids visited us. At one point, I walked out to the street to look around. No walker, no crutch – just me on my two legs. How invigorating, how glorious to be walking again.

As I strolled back up to the house, I heard horror-movie noises from across the street. Someone had rigged sound effects to go off whenever kids approached their door. How fun was that? I turned my head to look and – whoops! – I immediately lost my balance. Luckily, I was next to the house by then. Had the brick wall not been close enough for me to jerk out my right hand and steady myself, I certainly would have gone down for my first fall. Colleene was watching me. Dammit, she always catches moments like this, and then she has justification for the worrying she's so good at.

I suddenly had justification for worrying, myself. Half of all stroke victims suffer falls, and half of those falls result in new injuries. It had never occurred to me that turning my head while walking required so much of my brain. We develop these abilities very early in life, so we assume they are easy. Turns out, walking and chewing gum at the same time really is hard!

If you're not going through this yourself, imagine hiking down a steep, rocky hill with your eyes closed. Try walking downstairs backward without touching the handrail. Picture riding a bicycle while blindfolded. That's the wildly out-of-control sensation I had from turning my head while walking on a level sidewalk.

At my next PT session with Frank, I described my balance issue. I feel silly for thinking this now, but, at the time, I worried my unsteadiness was uncommon. I still did not appreciate that everything we take for granted, such as turning our heads while walking, is *learned*. Being a skilled expert in his field, Frank was fully prepared with an assortment of drills to help me relearn balance. Have I mentioned that Frank has a PhD in physical therapy? He's also impressively fit. Frank has the build of a tennis player and the agility of a ninja. Often, when he demonstrated an exercise he wanted me to do, I envied his youth and vitality. He made every movement look easy, effortless. Then I tried it and felt like a clod.

To develop my balance while walking, Frank and Bernie held flashcards with words printed on them. They flanked me as I strolled through the clinic, and Frank directed me where to look.

"Look up ... now read my flashcard ... look down ... now read Bernie's card ...."

The words on the flashcards were names of colors. To demand more focus, the words were written in colored ink that did not match the word. "Blue" might be written in red ink, "purple" in green ink, and so on. This made the exercise of reading each card more challenging and kind of fun, and doing it while walking was very effective at retraining my balance.

I liked this drill so much, and I could feel the benefit so well, that I found a way to incorporate Colleene's grandsons in a similar exercise at home. The boys had flashcards for practicing arithmetic. They walked along on either side of me, holding up their cards as I turned from side to side and computed the simple math equations. The practice sessions worked. At first, I could only perform this stunt at a dreadfully slow pace. Within a matter of days, I could walk briskly while shifting my gaze from side to side, up to down.

It's a shame we don't remember the earliest years of our lives. We have no recollection of being unable to balance ourselves or manipulate objects in our hands, so we take those fundamental skills for granted. Now that I've had to relearn so many basic abilities, I'm fascinated by watching babies learn those skills for the first time.

As adults, we don't give a second thought to buying a twenty-ounce cup of scalding hot coffee, removing the lid, and stirring in cream and sugar. Then we carry it to our car and sip it while driving. I am now aware that handling a hot beverage requires a spectacular level of brain-training. We wouldn't dream of handing a cup of scorching liquid to a two-year-old. Toddlers drink from "sippy" cups, which they repeatedly drop or tip over. Around age two they might progress to regular cups, but only partially filled, and those are cool drinks. We don't let kids touch hot beverages until age six or more. That's how long it takes our brains to learn the skill of sipping hot drinks without dumping scalding liquid on ourselves.

Advancements in technology have some worried that machines will replace humans. "Artificial Intelligence" is a popular theme in science fiction. I have a new appreciation for the incomprehensible complexity of a biological brain. Machines could not do what the brains of dogs and cats do, much less what human brains do, every moment of every day.

Sure, I've seen videos of walking, jumping robots. Machines already do many redundant chores for us. Computers may drive our cars for us within a few decades. But I doubt a robot will ever be built that can water ski, play tennis, or catch a Frisbee on the run.

Try to comprehend all that's happening in the brain of a football quarterback during a passing play. He's running away from the pursuit of giant men while looking downfield for an open receiver. When a receiver is spotted, the quarterback's brain instantly calculates distance and location. Electrical impulses tell the arm to throw a fifteen-ounce ball with the precise force, height, and trajectory to the target, and with a beautiful spiral. Oh, and the target is running, too, so the brain has to compute that into the placement of the pass. All this happens in nanoseconds.

No robot exists that could process merely a quarterback's vision during a pass play (focus, colors, shapes, rates of speed, distances) as fast as he does, much less running, throwing, balancing, and eluding defenders. The most sophisticated robots in the world can't do what a simple bumblebee can do.

The capacity of a one-terabyte computer hard drive seems massive. A typical laptop can store thousands of songs, movies, pictures, business documents, and e-mail messages. No one knows for sure, but scientists now believe a human brain can hold eighty *petabytes* of information. A petabyte is a thousand terabytes. One brain may be capable of containing as much information as eighty thousand one-terabyte hard drives. Computers are amazing, but brains are still thousands of times better.

10 Graduating To The Plateau

November was my best month yet. Movement was returning to all areas where it had been lost, balance was improving, and my speech became substantially better.

So much development did not escape the notice of Frank and Elsa. On Wednesday, November 20, eight days before Thanksgiving, they each subjected me to another evaluation. This time they were more stringent and judicious in measuring my progress. They were considering releasing me from therapy.

Range of motion, balance, and strength are the primary indicators. Elsa was first to examine me. Occupational therapists have devices that resemble an architect's tools for measuring range of motion. My left arm had regained almost full movement capacity in every direction except behind the back. These were huge improvements over not being able to lift my hand above my shoulder five months earlier. Arm strength and hand grip still had quite a way to go, but those parameters also showed excellent progress.

The moment of truth – it was time for the pegboard test again. First time I tried that test was two weeks after the stroke. At that point, I could hardly curl my fingers, could barely touch the tip of my index finger to my thumb. Elsa had stopped the test after it took me a minute and forty seconds to get one peg into a hole. In my second attempt two months later, I could get all the pegs into the holes and back out again, but it took over two minutes.

This time I completed the feat in forty-two seconds. That's still not as fast as the thirty second record I set with my right hand, but this was only five months after the stroke. Besides, I'll always be more dexterous with my right hand than my left.

Elsa put away the pegboard that had once been practically impossible and now seemed easy. She looked at me with uncharacteristic seriousness. "Do you feel ready to be released from occupational therapy?"

I grasped the gravity of her question. I was recovering well, probably would continue to recover well, but from this point on, if she released me from therapy, I'd be on my own. If I wanted more professional assistance, I'd need a doctor's referral. This wasn't simply closing a gym membership.

"I'm very motivated, and I'd like to think I do pretty well at working on my own," I replied, more as a question than a statement.

"Yes, you're good at doing your homework," she said, finally smiling.

"I'll miss seeing you all every week," I said, meaning it, "but I do feel ready to proceed on my own. Would you mind giving me your judgement on how well *you* think I can continue to recover?"

"We can't guarantee outcomes, whether you stay with therapy or not. I think you'll do very well. There's really not much more I can show you. Keep working on the things we've been doing, and you'll get a little better every month."

That was as good an answer as I could have anticipated. "In that case, I think I'm ready to graduate."

I had to sign several papers. Graduating from occupational therapy is quite an ordeal. I wanted to hug Elsa goodbye, but she was all business. We would part with a warm handshake – cordial and pleasant, but no hug. Melody and Reina, on the other hand, gave me enthusiastic hugs and gushed well wishes. I hugged them back with equal enthusiasm and gushed appreciation.

The significance dawned on me suddenly. I was done with occupational therapy. Within an hour, I might be done with physical therapy, too, and be entirely on my own for the remainder of my recovery.

But I had to get past the scrutiny of Frank next. I knew this would not be easy. Elsa was plenty tough. Frank was obsessive. I wouldn't have wanted any less from either of them.

Frank had his own range of motion tests. He repeated a technique he had used before to check my knee, which was to lean over and put his ear right above the joint, then have me bend and straighten my leg as much as I could. "Still have a popcorn thing going on in there," he observed. He had me do several tasks we had worked on in previous therapy sessions, but this time without assisting me. I climbed a few steps to a platform, which was still scary as hell without something to hold onto. Frank directed me to walk sideways, crossing one foot in front of the other, then reversing the steps. He measured muscle strength with leg presses and curls.

He also tried something he had not done before – a test Alex had done in the hospital five months earlier. Frank had me stand still as he shoved my shoulder, hard, from the front, side, back, and the other side. This is apparently a fairly standard method for testing balance. As with Alex, I was comfortably stable against Frank's nudges.

My balance was not so good when Frank asked me to stand on only my left foot. It was embarrassing that I could not hold my right foot off the floor for more than three seconds. Merely standing with all my weight on my left leg was an achievement. Balancing on my left foot continues to be difficult to this day. But, for the shoulder-shove test, I was solid as a rock. I could stand two-footed with excellent stability.

Then Frank had another new test for me, and this one was disastrous. He had me get on my hands and knees on a padded platform. This was trouble from the start. Simply being on "all fours" aggravated my weak knees. Frank asked me to stand up from that position. He wanted me to bring up my left leg, so that I was kneeling on the right knee, then stand up.

I brought the left leg up without too much trouble. But the moment I tried to stand, my knees gave out completely – both of them – with astonishing shocks of pain. Frank had apparently anticipated this, which was why he had me on the padded platform. I fell over on my side, bewildered by the weakness and severe pain in my knees.

"That's not the stroke. That's your lousy knees," he declared. "Next thing for you to do, soon as possible, is see an orthopedist. Therapy won't help those knees, and they won't get better on their own."

He got me righted on the platform and allowed me to sit for a moment to retrieve my senses while he typed on a computer keyboard.

"Congratulations, you've graduated. Keep doing what you're doing, get those knees taken care of, and you're going to be fine."

More paperwork to sign, a hug goodbye from Frank and Bernie, and I was finished. I began walking to the lobby, where Colleene was waiting. I made a show of carrying, not using, my crutch for Frank's benefit.

After a few steps, I turned and said to Frank and Bernie, "About two months ago, you said I'd be walking with no assistance in six weeks. If it hadn't been for these terrible knees, you'd have had me walking much sooner. Thanks." They smiled, and Bernie gave me a thumbs up.

Colleene and I waved goodbye to the good folks of UMC West physical therapy, and we went out to the car. I carried the crutch, did not use it, for the entire walk across the parking lot. Leaving physical therapy was significant. This meant I was nearing the end of what I call Stage Two of recovery.

Stage Three would be my left side progressing from being useful again to being normal again – fully adept and capable of everything it could do before the stroke. I'm still in Stage Three, probably will be for years.

Graduation from physical and occupational therapies took place the week before Thanksgiving. On Thanksgiving Day, Colleene and I went to the home of my cousin, Bill and his wife, Pam for the family get-together. Last time I had been to that house and seen the family had been four months earlier, at a reception for my cousin-once-removed, Courtney, who was visiting from Switzerland. At that point, I was still early in Stage One, bound to a wheelchair, barely able to curl the fingers of my left hand.

On Thanksgiving Day, I walked upright into the house. I took my crutch, in case I needed it, but it stood in a corner the entire time. I declined several offers of help and served my own plate of the festive feast from Pam's buffet. Admittedly, holding a large dinner plate in my left hand while serving food onto it with my right hand demanded more concentration than usual, but I managed it without leaving a trail of cranberry sauce and mashed potatoes on the floor.

Family members expressed awe and congratulated me on my impressive progress. But, amusingly, most seemed more taken aback by my beard. Last time I had shaved had been the day before the stroke. Five months of salt-and-pepper beard growth dramatically changed my appearance. One cousin teased I had quite a "Moses thing" going on.

The fall season of holidays is my very favorite time of year. I'm not avoiding the term "Christmas Season" to be politically correct; I'm referring to all the end-of-year festivities, from Halloween through New Year's Eve. I love fall weather, seasonal decorations, parties, all of it.

One of the best parts of fall celebrations is the food. I had been observing a very healthy, low calorie, plant-based diet since the beginning of the year, six months before the stroke. Having a stroke had compelled me to become even more strict about my food choices. The diet was working, too. I'd lost over fifty pounds, and all my health indicators had improved. For the holiday season, though, I took a break from dieting. I allowed ample indulgences in pumpkin pie, pound cake, and eggnog.

In December, Colleene and I enjoyed a night out for the first time in six months. We went to a movie. At the theater, I was pleased to discover I could climb stairs, albeit slowly and with a lot of effort. My balance still had a long way to go. I had to grip the handrail tightly and look straight down to climb a few stairs to our seats.

Later in the month, we attended a Christmas mixer, and we went to the family dinner get-together on Christmas Day. Each outing was wonderful for building my confidence and helping me feel normal again. Everyone who saw me and knew I'd had a stroke was quick to congratulate me on how far I had bounced back.

Each outing was also a stark reminder of how much remained for me to recover. Isn't that the way of life? It's one long series of gains and setbacks.

For New Year's Eve, Colleene and I took my dad out to dinner at an Italian restaurant. We enjoyed a delightful evening. This time I did not take a cane. I strolled through the restaurant totally unaided with ease. It felt terrific. But, as we left the restaurant and walked along the sidewalk, a young boy suddenly came running around a corner. He was out with his family and obviously having a grand time. The kid was at least ten feet away, so there was ample room to avoid a collision, but all of us, boy included, were a little startled and came to abrupt stops. I wasn't upset with the kid in the least. He was being a kid, having fun. But being startled and slamming on my brakes that way caused my left leg to jam. Instantly I lost my balance. I grabbed Colleene's shoulder to steady myself. I needed her stability for the remainder of our walk to the car. My leg continued to hurt, and my balance suffered a setback for several days.

The New Year's Eve encounter was frustrating. The rambunctious boy had not been close to plowing into me, yet the mere surprise of the youngster careening around a corner caused me to lose my balance. I thought I had made so much progress. Soon I would realize I had entered the "plateau" stage of recovery.

Many who read this may find it irritating that I had the nerve to be frustrated with my progress. Yes, I know how lucky I was. My stroke was mild, compared to others I have studied. My Uncle Lloyd never walked again after his stroke, and I was annoyed by balance issues after only six months. I should have been ecstatic that I was walking at all so soon. I am aware of that, and I frequently remind myself of it.

Whether I was luckier than others or not, being impaired is no fun. Besides, most people go their entire lives without having a stroke. Looking at it that way, I could argue I was pretty damned *un*lucky. Emotional fluctuations are part of any major medical condition. It's important to be aware of this. We should not ignore our states of mind while healing from diseases.

My state of mind was about to suffer a nosedive. I'll get to that shortly.

I may have allowed indulgences in my diet during the holiday season, but I did not relax my exercise regimen. Having graduated from physical therapy did not prompt me to slack off physical training at all. I replaced my two days a week of physical therapy with rigorous workouts at home. A steadfast resolve to continue progress pushed me to perform a little more each week. Furthermore, although I was no longer going to physical therapy, and even though I may never see them again, I did not want to disappoint Frank or Elsa or the rest of the UMC staff.

Starting the very first week after graduating from physical therapy – which was the week of Thanksgiving – I put myself on a schedule of training three days a week. The regimen continues to this day. At 1:00 PM every Monday, Wednesday, and Friday, I stop whatever I am doing and work out.

I've never been a fitness freak, but there was a time when I kept myself in pretty good shape. In my youth, an exercise routine would have included jumping rope, power-lifting heavy weights, and deep-squat knee bends. Now that my body has a few decades of wear and tear, and, oh yeah, I've had a stroke, my workouts are considerably less robust. Still, for a sixty-year-old guy, I think I put myself through a plenty respectable round of physical challenges.

When I started my home workout regimen in November, I would only do (*could* only do) twenty squats, and they were shallow squats at best. My early workouts included forty crunches, ten reps of lifting weights with each hand – twenty-five pounds with my right and a mere five pounds with my left. Five months later, I was up to fifty squats, a hundred crunches, and I could lift a ten-pound dumbbell above my head with my left arm. Every month or so I bumped up the number of reps.

I also used resistance straps in my workouts, marched around the back yard wearing ankle weights, and practiced several balance drills. These were the exercises I did from the beginning of my home therapy, and I continue with similar workouts to this day. The only things that have changed are how many reps I can do and how much weight I can lift. My strength and endurance for every challenge doubled from November to March, then doubled again from March to July. I became more physically fit than I had been in twenty years.

The "plateau" stage persists to this day. Glaciers flow down hillsides about as fast as my recovery progresses, but it's progressing, nonetheless. My brain is doing extensive work to rewire synapses and neurons. The "plateau" stage is common in stroke recovery. Seeing an apparent cease in progress can cause many to lose hope. I'd like to think of myself as a positive, never give up, can-do attitude kind of guy, but losing hope has a terrible effect on a person.

Throughout December, although I continued diligent workouts, my afflicted left limbs seemed to stop improving. It was my favorite time of year, as I've mentioned, and I had made lots of noticeable improvement up to then, so the slowed progress didn't impact my state of mind.

~ ~ ~ ~

The lack of visible progress continued into January, and then it did impact my state of mind. This was the nosedive I mentioned earlier. It's time to address another common element of stroke recovery – depression. This is difficult to write about. I don't like admitting to periods of depression, but leaving this out would be dishonest. Besides, overcoming the stigma of depression is the first step toward defeating depression. Most of us don't want to admit to being depressed. We don't want to seem weak or be perceived as annoying people who wallow in self-pity.

Perpetual victimhood may have become popular in modern society, but most people still prefer to feel capable and self-reliant. Going through life always feeling sorry for ourselves is unhealthy. Yet ignoring negative emotions and pretending nothing is ever wrong is more unhealthy.

Many mornings since the stroke, I woke up consumed with despair. Sometimes an overwhelming sense of gloom dropped over me in the middle of an afternoon and ruined the rest of my day. Part of this was pure neurology; my brain was not processing emotions properly because of the stroke. Understanding that did not make it feel better.

Depression is also triggered by discouragement, frustration, and chronic pain, all of which are common to a stroke sufferer. Many people in recovery wrestle with profound feelings of guilt for being a burden to others. Taking care of me was an enormous imposition on Colleene. Knowing what a strain I was sometimes made me bitter about my situation. The stroke impacted her almost as much as it impacted me, and I resented it for that.

Best method I've found to combat feeling like a burden is to appreciate my caregiver. Every day, the first thing I say to Colleene in the morning and the last thing I tell her at night is, "Thank you for everything you do for me."

Bitterness, frustration, depression – some think these negative emotions are things we should fight against. That is the wrong response. Suppressing undesirable feelings does not make them go away. In fact, denial of emotions can cause new infirmities. Stifling our feelings can literally make us sick. Negative emotions need to be addressed, processed, managed, not fought against.

January of 2020 marked the seventh month since my stroke. I repeat, I am aware how lucky I was and how fortunate I continue to be. I should have been thrilled that, in only six months, I had already recovered much of what the stroke took from me. Your situation may be so much worse than mine that it's beyond my comprehension. Let's be clear on this – I get it.

The point is, whatever stage of recovery a person is in, and for whatever disease, there will be periods of discouragement. Depression could be described as intensified discouragement, and it can be devastating.

A depressed person isn't sad. Sadness is grief. Sadness is caused by the death of a loved one, the end of a relationship, even a favorite restaurant closing. Depression is loss of hope. Depressed people rarely cry, and they often cannot articulate their states of mind. This is what makes depression so dangerous.

When our team loses a big game or when a dream vacation is canceled, we know why we are sad, and we know the sadness is temporal. Our despair is of the moment and in the moment. Like a sunburn or a bruise, we know what's causing the pain, and we know it will heal in time. Utter loss of hope is harder to understand. It's irrational to feel things will never get better, that a life has no chance to improve. Few conditions are totally insurmountable, no matter how awful. Yet, this is how depression feels and what it does to a person. It causes all-consuming hopelessness that can't be reasoned away.

Some people make the mistake of thinking a depressed person is simply sad or feeling low. It's much deeper and more troubling than that. Where depression and grief are similar is in our need to process them. We should not try to force ourselves to "snap out of" or "get over" depressing thoughts.

Someone who has lost a loved one needs to experience their grief, to go through the process. They should look at pictures of the one they lost, talk about treasured memories. This is how the brain deals with grief. In my experience, the same happens with depression. It should not be dismissed or ignored. We need to permit ourselves to feel lousy before we can feel hopeful again.

You wouldn't dream of telling a grieving person who has lost a loved one, "Cheer up! Things will get better. Everyone dies eventually. Might as well move on with your life!" Those would be horrible things to say to someone who's suffered a loss. Yet we commonly think we should tell a depressed person, "Hey, buck up. Things aren't so bad. You'll get better some day. Quit moping around. Things could be a lot worse!"

When things are terrible, considering how much worse things *could* may seem helpful, but it does not address the real issue. It is not comforting to tell a depressed person, "Look on the bright side. Pull yourself together." More helpful is to dig into depression and understand the loss of hope. Go ahead and examine it, let it out. A person in a state of depression should allow themself to process their negative emotions. They should look for the thing they're most afraid of or disturbed by, then try to figure out what would overpower that disturbing feeling. When we find something to hope for, no matter how insignificant, we need to grab onto that morsel of faith. Focus on that. In time, other things to hope for will start popping up.

~ ~ ~ ~

Before I continue this topic, allow me to clarify: I am not a psychiatrist, nor do I claim to be a medical expert of any kind. I am relating my own experiences and those of other people who shared their experiences with me. Do not avoid or reject the advice of medical professionals because of something I suggest.

~ ~ ~ ~

Most of my career life was in the radio business. Like musicians or actors, only a select few make big bucks in broadcasting. I was not one of those select few, but it was a heck of a fun way to barely earn a living. One of the most satisfying parts of the job was interviewing interesting people. In 2009, I interviewed Kenny Rogers. Whether you're a fan of his country-pop tunes or not, it's hard to dispute that Kenny was among the most famous people of the twentieth century. He also was one of the nicest, most genuine celebrities I ever got to meet.

In 2009, Kenny Rogers was seventy-one, and he had undergone major knee surgery, yet he continued to tour the country and make appearances on TV shows. In our interview, I asked what kept him going. How did he keep up the pace after fifty years in the business? His reply was wonderful.

"Happiness comes down to three things: We need someone to love, something to do, and something to hope for."

I knew at the time Kenny was quoting something I had heard before. I wasn't sure where I'd heard it, but it was a familiar saying. Mr. Rogers never claimed credit for that nugget of philosophy; he just repeated it as a worthy way of approaching life. I like to use the story of my interview with Kenny Rogers to relay the credo he quoted, because it makes the concept more fun and relatable.

A quick internet search reveals the quote is originally credited to an eighteenth-century philosopher named

Immanuel Kant, who called those three principles the "Rules for happiness."

Those three "Rules" are, I believe, equal in value to every human's well-being. It may seem we could do without one, so long as we have the other two. Two-thirds is more than half, so shouldn't that be enough? No, not in my experience. Those three principles of life are like the legs of a three-legged stool; if one is missing, the stool does not stand up.

In my case, a large part of hopelessness was due to feeling worthless. Even if I did recover from the stroke – completely recover, as if it never happened – I would be in my sixties and practically broke. What could I possibly do to bring in an income? Who would hire me?

Then it occurred to me unemployed people feel this kind of discouragement all the time. It wasn't only the stroke that made me feel inadequate. Most of us need to feel productive, that we are pulling our own weight. Sure, some people go through life always depending on others. I find it hard to comprehend a person who expects to be provided for and make no meaningful contributions their entire life. Being productive is essential to feeling fulfilled. To be clear, I don't suggest a person needs to work a job to make a contribution. Earning a paycheck isn't the only way to be productive. Homemakers and caregivers are important contributors, male or female, traditionally employed or not.

Realizing what caused much of my lack of hope prompted me to do something about it. I started looking for useful things to do. Doing that led to a profound change in my mental state. Motivational speakers promote this constantly: Our lives are built through doing. If we do nothing, nothing will change, and our subconscious minds know that. Seems simple when we look at it this way, but it's fundamental to how our minds work. Doing – being active and productive – leads to positive thoughts and outcomes.

And there it is: "Something to do" is one of Immanuel Kant's (and Kenny Rogers') rules of happiness.

What to do may be unclear, which often leads us to choose inaction. Doing nothing means doing nothing wrong. It also means doing nothing right. Finding something productive to do, doing anything that would generate a desirable outcome, was enormously beneficial for conquering depression, in my experience.

One time I went through my desk drawers and threw away all the old, non-working pens. I organized notepads, consolidated paperclips and boxes of staples. It was the kind of chore we all want to do but easily put off. Who has the time? In stroke recovery, one thing we have a lot of is idle time. Doing simple chores made my idle time feel productive. And how rewarding it was to eliminate jobs from the "To Do" list that I had been procrastinating for years. Now, months after that day of organizing, opening a desk drawer gives me a delightful sense of satisfaction.

Healing takes time, whether it's for a wound in the flesh or in the mind. The process of mending can be difficult, but ignoring an injury means it may not heal. When negative thoughts creep up, I find it best to confront them, deal with them, allow myself to feel them.

Wish I could say depression is something we deal with once, and then it goes away. I feel silly to admit it, but I used to think that. I believed in being optimistic, focusing on the positive, shunning negative thoughts. Depression is a problem for weak-minded people. How foolishly unrealistic I was.

If someone we care about dies, we feel deep sorrow. Our heart aches. Even the toughest macho guys are expected to feel sad when they lose someone they care about. We should accept depression and discouragement the same way.

Grief may hurt for months, but in time we move on. Does that mean we expect never to feel sorrow again? Ridiculous. We forever miss loved ones we lose. We grieve for every cherished person who leaves us. One of the things I hate most about growing old is losing people I care about.

Grief is triggered by a specific event, something we can identify. It could be the death of a loved one, a canceled vacation, the last child moving away from home. When sadness hits, we usually know what causes it. Depression can sneak up on us for no apparent reason. That's partly why the feeling is hard to understand and deal with.

Again, I am not a psychiatrist and don't pretend to know every situation. I can only relate my experience. Some days, depression came over me like a thick fog. I couldn't clear my thoughts from dark clouds of despair. I've been discouraged before. Like anyone, I've known disappointment over not being chosen for a job or dejection from being fired from a job – several jobs, actually. Some disheartening events in the past prompted me to over-indulge in food and booze as a way of soothing my misery. I've also known bleakness that had the opposite effect; simple pleasures lost their appeal. Food wasn't satisfying, favorite TV shows became uninteresting, music was tedious. We all experience discouragement and despair. That's why we have words for those emotions. Yet, on my worst days of the past, when everything seemed gloomy, when I felt pale, impotent, and empty inside, a part of me knew things would get better somehow. I just needed to hold on and stick to it.

The days of depression that followed my stroke brought similar lackluster feelings, but this time I didn't feel better days were ahead. My future seemed to offer no possibility of fun or fulfillment. This was an unbearable prospect, and very unfamiliar to me.

For a time, I tried to struggle against the despair, to wrestle it out of my mind, overcome it, fight against it. That was the wrong approach. We think of feelings as intangible devices that occur in our souls. The expression "have a heart" is a euphemism for "show some feeling" or "have compassion." Logically, we know a heart has no feeling or compassion. It's an organ that pumps blood. Emotions happen in the brain. Joy and sorrow, triumph and despair, anger and delight; all emotions are electrical impulses darting around in our brains.

My dear friend Bill in Nashville reminded me emotions happen in the brain, and my brain had taken damage. (Bill is gloriously gay and full-fledged Southern. It gives context to explain he speaks with a distinct Tennessee accent and with the flamboyance of a fashion designer.) This is what he told me in a phone call:

"Dahling, you've had a strrroooke! What DID you expect? Your *brain* needs to heal, and *you* need to let it!"

Thank goodness for the people who care about us. Bill's advice took hold. Depression didn't suddenly leave the scene and not bother me again. Days of despondency continued to plague me, but I learned to tell myself it was a healing process my brain needed to go through. Neurons and synapses were out of whack. Things would get better. My gray matter needed to repair itself first. An injury to my brain was producing my gloom. I didn't try to "snap out of it" or force myself to feel better. Yet I also did not allow the negative thoughts to overwhelm me.

Depression can lead a mind to very dark places. It's okay to feel bad sometimes. It's not okay to let bad feelings progress to bad actions. The bad feelings will pass. Some bad actions are irreversible. If you find yourself trapped by feelings of gloom, if the bad feelings don't pass, talk to someone.

Most days, when depression made an unwelcome appearance, I focused on the certain things I could hope for. Depression wanted to take away my hope, so I doubled down my concentration on enjoyable activities I could look forward to, regardless my condition. Directing my attention to things as simple as TV shows I wanted to watch or a good dinner I expected to have helped spur my mind away from depressive thoughts.

And I focused on doing. If I wasn't up to working my freelance job, I organized boxes in the garage, cleaned the patio, or went for a walk. Sometimes I played computer games to occupy myself, but I discovered greater benefit came from doing things that resulted in a sense of accomplishment. For me, finally doing a dreaded project I'd been putting off was good therapy for overcoming depression.

The plateau stage continues to this day and will probably be my state for several years. It doesn't discourage me now the way it did a few months ago, because now I'm used to it. It was terribly frustrating to detect precious little improvement in my strength and stability for months at a time. As I neared the first anniversary of the stroke, I watched some of my early videos. I had made videos of myself for exactly this purpose – to track my development – and it worked. Good lord, I had made tremendous progress! It had slowed to such a gradual pace, I couldn't perceive it from week to week, but the person I had become was far more capable than the person I was when I made those videos.

This was my status at the one-year mark after the stroke. Another calamity arrived during the ninth month of recovery, so let's back up a bit.

11 Along Came A Virus

What a year 2020 turned out to be, huh? If I never hear "We're all in this together" again, it will be too soon. My editor Tammy told me the expression she found most tiresome was "In these unprecedented times...." Which worn-out pandemic platitude did you find most annoying?

Yes, I get it; coronavirus was a serious disease that warranted a serious response. But people around the world acted as if the sky was falling. Emergency Alerts were sent to our cell phones telling us not to visit our moms on Mother's Day. Can you believe that? The EAS was originally created to warn against a nuclear attack. (Back then it was called EBS – Emergency Broadcast System.) Later, its main purpose became an alert for tornadoes and hurricanes. In 2020, EAS was activated to tell us not to see our moms.

Decades from now, historians will examine whether the extreme measures of 2020 were justified. Regardless which side you fall on – if you think it was too much or not enough – the severe reactions to the virus caused widespread destruction to humans everywhere. Some suffered setbacks from which they will never recover. Others were damaged but will rebound. Amazingly, being in stroke recovery meant I was among the few who suffered no damage. A disability made me one of the lucky ones.

Like giant breaker switches turning off one by one, the shut-down took place in stages. I'm sure you remember when and how the paranoia first began to affect your life. It started in early March here in the US. Kids who were out of school for spring break were told to extend the break an extra week. Then it was two weeks, three weeks, and then it was the entire remainder of the school year. Weddings were postponed, vacations canceled, restaurants and stores closed, jobs lost. By April, most of the planet's humans were hiding from each other.

Meanwhile, here was little ol' me, and I'd been "sheltering in place" for eight months already. Being stuck at home had become my new normal. I hadn't driven a car since June of 2019. My entire existence rarely required stepping out of about eight hundred square feet of living space.

Colleene works from home doing medical billing. She never had to miss a single day of work, nor a single paycheck. Her daughter-in-law works an "essential" job, and her office arranged adequate distancing between cubicles. She also did not miss a single paycheck. It's terrifying to imagine the hardships we would have faced if any of our incomes had been lost due to the pandemic paranoia.

This had a strange effect on me. The realization that I was getting along fine while millions of people's lives were being destroyed made me feel a peculiar sense of good fortune. For weeks I had contended with bouts of depression that I couldn't shake. One of those emotions was the classic "Why did this happen to me?" The pandemic prompted a distinct feeling of "So glad that *didn't* happen to me!"

Note I am referring to the reactionary lock-down to the virus, not the virus itself. Less than one percent of the world population actually got the disease in 2020, and less than two percent of them died from it. The *lock-down* over the disease was the wide-spread destroyer of lives, and that's the thing I felt so lucky to avoid.

Looking at my situation with that perspective may be going out on a limb to see myself as lucky, but it worked. As the lock-down dragged on for a second month (citations issued to people who held family dinners for Easter), third month (better not see Mom for Mother's Day and no Memorial Day picnics!), fourth month (phone calls only to Dad on Father's Day), FIFTH month (July Fourth Parades cancelled); the longer the pain lasted for most other people, the more I appreciated my good fortune. And the more regret I felt for the millions enduring serious hardship.

To paraphrase an old expression, "I felt sorry for myself because I had no shoes, until I met a person who had no feet." My life had been stalled for months before coronavirus hysteria started. Seeing the rest of the world go through a devastating shutdown gave me a peculiar sense of euphoria – a profound relief that, thanks to a stroke, pandemic paranoia had almost no impact on my life. That's not to say I was glad the rest of the world suffered. This wasn't a vindictive sense of glee that, since I was enduring a hardship, I was glad others were suffering, too. That would be a horrible attitude.

Yet, there was solace in recognizing how much better off I was than others. Some folks lost small businesses that had been in their families for decades. Others saw their retirement savings evaporate or had to give up their homes. A little brain damage was all that had happened to me. The shut-down inflicted little more than an annoyance to my life, thanks to a stroke. How bizarre is that?

My heart goes out to all who were hurt by the oppressive lock-down of 2020. Hope your recovery is going well.

Perhaps stalling the world for several months was the appropriate course. We may decide that slowing the virus was worth ruining millions of households. Regardless, I couldn't resist seeing the humor when people wore face masks while driving their cars to go buy hand sanitizer. Driving a car was significantly more likely to cause death or injury than the virus. I'm sure some of my fears are irrational, too.

Meanwhile, my plateau stage continued. While people around the world were enduring financial ruin and not being allowed to visit loved ones, my life hardly changed. I coasted through the months of lock-down with the same day-to-day activities as before it started. It was peculiar to feel lucky for having had a stroke.

~ ~ ~ ~

The plateau stage is more a gradual incline than a flat plain, but I understand why stroke victims call it that. Progress becomes so slow, it's imperceptible. Months go by with no real noticeable advancement.

Progress was minimal from month to month, but it was progress. I was glad I made videos to track my development. When I became discouraged because my hand was still clumsy or my shoulder still hurt, I brought up prior videos to see how much worse I had been, and how much better I had become.

In December, right after graduating from physical therapy, I still could not lift five pounds above my head with my left arm. I had to remind myself that lifting my arm at all was an improvement. Still, I couldn't help feeling frustrated some days as weakness in my left arm persisted into January and February.

I kept doing empty-handed arm lifts. It felt silly at times, merely lifting my empty hand above my head, but the effort finally paid off. In the last week of February, almost eight months after the stroke, I hoisted a five-pound weight above my head with my left hand. It was a satisfying moment of triumph.

Lifting a small, pink dumbbell above my head felt only slightly less silly than lifting no weight at all, but I kept at it. Three months later, in the first week of May, I became strong enough to lift ten pounds. It seemed to take forever, but when I looked back, I realized I was being impatient through the slow stages of progress. It's like time-lapse photography of a flower blooming. Changes that are imperceptible in real time seem brisk in sped-up retrospective.

Having a timeline of recovery videos helps me keep a healthy perspective on my recovery and on life in general. Again, I realize how fortunate I am, and that helps keep me positive. I've discovered stories of stroke victims whose recoveries took decades, and they suffered disabilities much more disruptive than mine. I can't imagine losing the ability to speak. My speech was slightly diminished, but I was never unable to converse with family and friends. That must cause a person to feel terribly isolated.

My recovery seemed to drag in the spring of 2020, but, during that same period, millions of other people saw their lives utterly destroyed. Being in stroke recovery made me a lucky person, indeed, compared to so many devastated by the shutdown.

12 Strange Anniversary To Celebrate

Today is June 29, 2020. I am writing this chapter on the first anniversary of my stroke. One year ago today was the last time I had full use of my left side. That day I strode into a hospital unassisted, completely upright and on my own power. I'd been through a series of transient ischemic attacks the night before. There was reason for concern, of that I was certain, but all my parts were still operating. I thought my hospital visit would take a few hours. A doctor might tell me to improve my diet and get more exercise, and that would be that.

Six days later, I came home from the hospital in an ambulance. I could not stand, walk, or even sit up without help. My left hand was so swollen it looked like a latex glove filled with water. In short, I was an invalid. And I did not know how long I would remain that way.

Physical therapists at the hospital had been very encouraging. They were confident I would regain most, if not all, my abilities with time and steadfast therapy. I might be fully recovered in a year, or it might be a year before I could simply walk again, but they asserted I should recover.

And now it's been a year. Becoming whole again is happening between the hospital therapists' best and worst predictions. Full recovery is still a good way off, but I've been walking for over six months. My left hand is clumsy, but I can open jars and button a shirt. It will be months, maybe a few more years, before I'm rebuilt enough to work a regular job again. But I feel confident now that I will be able to work again. I've come to terms with the possibility that some strength and coordination may never come back.

This is not an event I ever anticipated observing on an annual basis, but, what the hell, since I am recovering, might as well celebrate it. Tonight, Colleene and I will pop open a bottle of champagne. Recovery truly began on the day I returned home from the hospital, so we plan to celebrate again on July 5. We're going to take an indulgent break from my healthy diet; breakfast will be a pile of doughnuts, dinner will be platters of nachos with Tecate beers. Yeah, that's how to celebrate stroke recovery West Texas style!

I've never had a stroke before, so I don't know how typical my recovery is. What I do know is brain damage confounds anyone it afflicts. No one can anticipate how life will change after a stroke. It's not the kind of thing we prepare for. Losing neurons affected me in ways that are still confusing a year later. Here are a few of the more confounding side effects:

Taking off my left boot: Around the house, I wear goofy old man sneakers with Velcro straps. I can put those on and take them off with ease now. No help needed from Colleene. On the rare occasions when we go out, I like to wear boots. I can put boots on by myself. It's still difficult and clumsy, but I can put on footwear by myself. This is a huge improvement over not being able to put on socks a few months ago. However, I *cannot* take off my left boot by myself. This is baffling. I can bring my left foot up and rest it on my right knee. I can grasp the boot heel in my right hand, of course – the stroke affected my left side, not right – but my left foot refuses to relax to release the boot.

Last week, Colleene and I took my dad out to brunch for Father's Day. I wore boots for the occasion. We hadn't been out in a while, so I hadn't worn boots in a while. I was certain by then I could remove my left boot without assistance. I was wrong.

The synapses that control my left foot are still misfiring. Instead of relaxing my foot – so it points out and the boot can slide off – the moment I take hold of the boot, my foot pulls up tight and locks in place, such that the boot simply will not slide off. I struggled with it for a good ten minutes, then had to stop and take a break. Colleene kept offering to help. For some reason, when she pulls off the boot, my foot allows itself to relax, and the boot comes off with ease. When I try it, my foot will not let the boot come off. Another part of the problem is my hamstring continues to be surprisingly weak. The hamstring is the muscle that pulls the lower leg up under the body, which is how we extract a foot out of a boot. I never appreciated how much that muscle is needed for boot removal.

After a break, I attacked the boot again, this time with heightened determination. Another ten minutes of strenuous effort, and I had to give up. My left leg was beginning to cramp and hurt. Colleene to the rescue. I stretched out my left leg, she took hold of the boot and pulled it off my stubborn left foot in two seconds.

Stability: I have been standing and walking without a crutch or any other assistance for six months, yet I often need to steady myself, as if I stood up too fast from bending over. This usually happens when I look up or turn quickly. My brain has trouble keeping up with rapid movement of my head.

I have an old friend named Curtis, a fellow disc jockey who lives in the Boston area. He calls me "Jahvis," and we routinely disagree on proper pronunciation of common words, such as "route." Curtis argues it's always pronounced "root," as in the classic song "Route 66." I contend it's sometimes pronounced "rowt," as in the power tool that cuts grooves into wood, called a router.

Curtis, who is about my age, assured me the slight dizziness comes with advancement of years. It's one of the many penalties we face for getting older. He sometimes experiences full-on vertigo as he approaches Seasoned Citizen status.

Other friends have shared experiences with losing equilibrium as they age, which is both comforting and disconcerting at the same time. I'm relieved my instability may not be a long-lasting effect from the stroke, but that's little reassurance if occasional dizziness means I'm declining into an old geezer!

Persistent left-handed clumsiness: Occupational therapist Elsa advised me hands are usually the last afflicted areas to recover after a stroke. Our human hands are so complex, the area of the brain that controls them needs extensive time to repair. I did not regain the dexterity to hold up three fingers with my left hand until almost ten months into recovery. I could do one, two, or all four, but keeping the pinky down while holding up three fingers in the shape of a "W" was an ability that required ten months of hand exercises. At one year since the stroke, my left hand has finally developed almost the same range of motion as my right hand. What it lacks is coordination.

I'm right-handed, so, naturally, my left hand will never be as coordinated as my right. Simple motions, though, that the left hand should perform still elude me. It's difficult to pet or play with our dog left-handed. A few nights ago, I discovered my left hand could not pour wine from a bottle. Lifting the bottle triggered pain in my wrist, and, when I started to pour, my arm was so wobbly I switched hands to avoid a spill.

Shaking pepper is still frustrating. This is really perplexing. I can pick up a pepper shaker left-handed and unscrew the lid to refill it, both of which were impossible a few months ago. But it feels as if the container weighs ten pounds when I try to shake it with my left hand. The rapid back-and-forth movement requires more coordination than my left arm has at this point. I keep practicing. It takes half a minute to add pepper to a salad. I sometimes have to grit my teeth and resist the urge to grab the shaker with my right hand to hurry things along. I've learned to accept the slow process of regaining muscle abilities.

~ ~ ~ ~

Now it's July 5, the other significant anniversary to my experience of a stroke. A year ago today I came home from the hospital in an ambulance.

It's been one heck of a week since I started this chapter. Last year, I spent the first week of July worsening each day, declining from a fully functional middle-aged man to a non-functioning invalid. This year, I consciously did the opposite. Last Monday, the day I started this chapter, I shaved my beard and got a haircut for the first time in a year. My greying beard had become bushy and ridiculous. Transforming from that to a clean-shaven face resulted in a rather astonishing change to my appearance. All week since, Colleene has been doing double-takes every time she sees me. She often jokes, "Who are you, and what are you doing in my house?"

Everyone at the haircut franchise shop was wearing a face mask. We're still in coronavirus hysteria. I dutifully wore a mask, too. The girl who cut my hair suggested I had enough length in back to go for a full mullet. I chuckled, then realized she was serious. "Wait, I assumed hair stylists hated mullets."

"Oh, no," she said, peering pleasantly over her face mask, "I think the mullet is a cool style."

I didn't want to hurt her feelings, but I also did not care to look like Joe Dirt. "Ah, well, maybe I'll grow it back out later. For now, I'd like to clear out all the over-growth." Some tufts of hair she cut off were over six inches long. The shave and haircut dramatically changed my look, to be sure.

When we returned home from my haircut, I drove the car, another thing I hadn't done in a year. I have an appointment with the Department Of Motor Vehicles to take the driver test tomorrow. It seemed a good idea to do some practice driving before I attempted the test. I was right. My driving was decidedly uncertain; turns were too wide or shallow, and I lurched coming to stops. The stroke still caused a little weakness in the left arm, which affected my steering. Colleene and I worried I might not be ready to drive yet, which was discouraging.

Turned out, my inept driving was from being out of practice, not from stroke-induced disabilities. In the few days since that first lackluster attempt, I've gone along on grocery shopping trips and other errands, and I've done the driving. For extra practice, I pulled into an empty parking lot (plenty of wide open lots around these days, thanks to coronavirus shutdown), and I worked on cornering, backing, and parking. Within twenty minutes my confidence and control were coming back. I'll let you know how I do on the test tomorrow. Last time I took a driver test was in 1975. The officer who administers the test tomorrow likely was not born yet when I got my first driver's license.

I expected it would be fun to celebrate the anniversary of my stroke. Losing the grey beard and shaggy hair were supposed to be ceremonies to mark milestones in my recovery. Instead, the sudden flurry of activities triggered unexpected anxieties.

First, simply shaving my beard and getting a haircut made me nervous. Not just a little nervous, I was jittery. I had foregone shaves and haircuts for convenience. It seemed silly to bother shaving when I couldn't even take a shower after the stroke. Later, my bushy beard and shaggy hair became symbols of my recovery. Removing those symbols represented changing my status. Was I ready to change my rank from "recovering" to "recovered"? Could I handle the expectations of being a normal person again? Also, it had become kind of fun to skip shaving and haircuts. I'd been on a year-long holiday from personal grooming. Eventually, of course, I had to do something. I was beginning to look like a caveman. But on June 29, I thought perhaps ending my vacation from shaving could wait a few more weeks. I had no idea removing my symbols of recovery would arouse so much angst.

More than being a symbol of my recovery, a full beard had become part of my look. Shaving it would drastically change my appearance. A bushy salt-and-pepper beard made me look like an old guy who was allowed to be weak and disabled, someone from whom not much was expected. I was comfortable with being perceived as frail.

Stroke recovery in general had become my identity. Almost everything I did related to overcoming a stroke. All activities were therapy. Every time I consciously used my left hand to grasp a doorknob, pick up a book, turn on a lamp, drink from a glass – every left-handed motion was a deliberate exercise. Walking through the house, stepping in from the patio, putting on shoes, buttoning a shirt – all actions had been brain-training for a year.

Graduating from the recovery state of mind was like taking the training wheels off a bicycle or swimming into the deep end of the pool for the first time. I knew I was ready for it. I'd been eagerly anticipating it. But the actual day of commencement made me far more nervous than I expected. Observing the anniversary of my stroke bought on as much anxiety as fun.

It also was more tiring than I expected. We don't realize how much energy our day-to-day activities require, until we stop doing them. I hadn't gone grocery shopping or run errands or done hardly anything outside the house for a year. I had been doing strenuous workouts three days a week, so my physical stamina was actually higher than before the stroke. I thought my energy level would be ample for driving, errand-running, and other out-of-house activities. Mental energy is altogether different from physical stamina, I learned. After driving home from my haircut, I needed to come right in and take a nap. The simple act of driving demands concentration, focus, coordination; all of which use mental energy, and our brain's endurance diminishes with lack of use.

I've often thought one of the reasons we slow down as we age is because we slow down as we age. Our minds can't do as much because we stop asking our minds to do as much. In young adulthood, the bustle of daily life keeps us sharp and maintains our mental stamina. From the moment we get up, our days are crammed with brain-demands. We get ourselves dressed, tend to children, drive in traffic to work, concentrate on our jobs, have lunch with colleagues, drive in traffic back home, stop for groceries on the way. When we stop doing, doing, doing, our brains atrophy, just as unused muscles do.

My workouts had become strenuous enough that I was in better physical condition a year after the stroke than the day before the stroke. I'll never say something so silly as I'm glad the stroke happened. Some self-help gurus suggest we should be cheerful about everything that happens to us. We're supposed to rejoice when we stub a toe or have a flat tire or break a window. That kind of Pollyanna thinking strikes me as absurd. I most certainly am not glad I had a stroke. However, when bad things happen, it does make sense to seek the best outcome. One very good outcome from my stroke is it compelled me to get into shape.

Jarvis Hooten

That's all well and good, and I am in better physical shape now than before the stroke, but my mental activity slacked off considerably while I focused on recovery. I'd been retraining my brain to control the left side of my body. Now that my left side is functional again, I'm surprised to discover how much stamina was lost in other areas of my brain.

Recovery isn't over yet. After a year of struggle and determination, I'm functional again, but I'm nowhere near normal again. Therapy in one form or another will continue for years.

Still Writing Final Chapters

No two people are exactly alike, so no two strokes are exactly alike. Our brains are vastly sophisticated. My experiences will not be identical to any other survivor of brain damage.

Our trials may not be the same, but the ways we rebound share similarities. My adventure with stroke recovery is now in its second year. Almost every day still begins with stubborn feelings of despair. I've grown accustomed to being rather glum for the first half hour of my day. My brain doggedly reminds me of fun activities I may never get to do again. Why did this have to happen to me? Will I ever be able to travel again, be productive again, do *anything* fun again? These stubborn emotions invade my mind almost every morning as I wake up.

Countering negative thoughts is now part of my daily routine, and I've become pretty good at it. Colleene often joins in the act. I remind myself how much worse off I could be. She points out how far I have come, and how much farther I will surely progress in the future. By the time I finish my second cup of coffee, I'm usually ready to try optimism again.

Many brain injury survivors are much worse off than I am. I don't believe it's productive to go through life with a perpetual attitude of "things could be worse," but it does help keep my situation in perspective. Compared to most brain injury victims, I am exceedingly fortunate.

Last week I took my driver's license test, as I mentioned in the last chapter. This was something I never expected to do a second time. My license happened to expire two months after the stroke. If the expiration date had been a year later, I could have renewed it as anyone else does without needing to retake the driving test. With the expiration occurring when it did, I doubt they'd renew my license if someone rolled me into the DMV in a wheelchair.

In Texas, acquiring a driver's license now involves reviewing a video series on distracted driving. I hope other states are doing this, too. It was quite impactful. The videos told the stories of several people who had been in horrific traffic accidents caused by distracted driving. Some caused the accidents themselves; others were victims of distracted drivers.

The stories that affected me most, naturally, were of folks who suffered brain injuries from car crashes. One nice-looking fellow was nineteen years old when he was riding as a passenger in a car. The driver picked up his phone to read a text. That split second of distraction was all it took. The resulting crash caused massive brain damage to the nineteen-year-old. Before the accident, he'd been a recent high school graduate, about to start college at UT Austin with his whole life ahead of him. After the accident, he was a quadriplegic, unable to talk, walk, or feed himself. His only way of communicating was through a computer that spoke for him.

Through the robotic voice of his computer, this young fellow described how he often thought of guiding his motorized wheelchair into a nearby swimming pool and drowning himself. Damage to the brain causes such thoughts. My brain injury happened forty years later in life, and mine was trivial, compared to that young fellow's, yet I also wrestled with thinking the unthinkable.

The video series about distracted driving had a dual impact on me. It made me appreciate how much worse my brain damage could have been, and, as intended, it made me highly more aware of the dangers of distracted driving. I wasn't a fool who would text and drive, but I did occasionally take a phone call while driving. Never again. The DMV's video scared the heck out of me.

Oh, and yes, I passed the driver test. As I suspected, the woman who administered the test had not yet been born when I got my first driver's license.

~ ~ ~ ~

A stroke or tragic accident can cause a person to feel useless, that their life is no longer worth living. A moment of misfortune can end a life or make a life feel it has ended. A disaster can happen to anyone at any time. An instant of bad luck can change a person forever.

Conversely, I can think of dozens of people who have

glorious advantages in life through sheer, dumb luck. Paris Hilton, the Kardashians, you know the type – vacuous, insufferable dullards who never know a day of hardship. How galling it is when those fortunate ones complain of trivial adversity. Perhaps an affliction is good for us; it makes us appreciate what we have. Luck gives to some and takes away from others. We have no control over luck. We only control how we manage the luck given to us, good or bad.

Negative thoughts since the stroke have distressed me over both my past and future. I don't know how many stroke victims are affected this way. For me, as often as I felt discouraged about the life that lay ahead, I also deeply regretted the life that lay behind.

We all have regrets. That's natural. Only a superficial person without a conscience claims to have no regrets. The stroke amplified my regrets. When negative emotions overtook my thoughts, every big choice I ever made seemed dreadful and egregious. My angry mind told me I'd wasted my life, carelessly hurt people I cared about, and utterly failed to reach my potential. How foolish I had been in my work life, how neglectful I had been in my personal life.

Often in the past year I have lain awake in the middle of the night dumbfounded by remorse. What a buffoon I have been! How could I have wasted my youth on so many meaningless pursuits? How could I not see who and what were truly important?

Such unwelcome emotions sometimes invaded my thoughts before the stroke, too, of course. We all sometimes wish we could change things in our pasts.

Most of us don't discuss these thoughts openly, so I don't know how common my experience was. For me, after the stroke, confronting regret became overwhelming and unbearable. I could not turn off the "should have done" demons.

It's a grim picture I'm painting of stroke recovery, isn't it? This is not to scare you or fill you with dread – quite the opposite. I want others who are contending with these thoughts to know they are not alone. Negative emotions are common and natural after a brain injury. Our synapses are misfiring, neurons are reconnecting.

Like everything else that happens in the brain, emotions are electrical impulses that zip around among our neurons. You will not feel the same regrets or despair I felt. Each of us recovers from stroke in our own way. But you likely will be disoriented by mental states that are unfamiliar.

After brain damage, we have to relearn how to use parts of our bodies. I had to train my left hand to grasp and hold things again. My left leg had to learn to walk and balance again. Frequently, to this day, I struggle to speak in smooth, fluid sentences. My brain is working to re-learn those abilities.

Likewise, processing emotions is a function the brain *learns*. It isn't inherent to our natures from birth. Think of how a small child overreacts to trivial disappointment, or how a teenager's world falls apart over being snubbed by a crush. A sixteen-year-old is well into his or her second decade of life, yet their brain is still learning to process emotional stress. Managing our feelings is learned. Brain damage commonly impairs both physical and mental abilities.

It's okay to have bad days. It's normal to encounter difficult emotions. We experienced discouragements and regrets before brain damage, and our minds had learned how to contend with those adversities. After brain damage, a mind needs to retrain itself to process the troubles of life. It's difficult, often very unpleasant, and it takes a disturbingly long time, but this is how our brains work. We have to allow the process to happen at its own pace. Let the people around you know about the feelings you are struggling with, so they can better understand your uncharacteristic moodiness. Stroke recovery can be as hard on the caregivers as it is on the victim.

I have three reasons for writing this book. First, I hope to bring hope. Damage to the brain often leads to stifling despair. We can become so disheartened by our affliction we lose sight of future possibilities. No matter how much or how little a person recovers from a stroke, I believe every life has prospects for happiness and purpose.

Second, I hope my story brings encouragement. You may wonder how that differs from wanting to bring hope. Encouragement and hope are different things. In my experience, courage precedes hope. Courage is the foundation for hope. We can't very well be optimistic about the future if we are afraid of it. The prefix "en-" means "to cause or bring about." I hope sharing my story will cause or bring about courage to others who are in similar circumstances, and I hope courage strengthens their will to feel hopeful.

Third, and perhaps most important, this book is intended to offer understanding. I've discovered damage to the brain affects a person differently from damage to any other part of the body. I've had broken bones and gashes that required stitches. Those injuries were painful and involved weeks of healing, but no trauma to the flesh caused the emotional impact of the stroke.

Almost any organ can be transplanted. We could be kept alive by the liver or a lung from another human, but it would not change our individuality. We could lose our arms and legs, our eyesight, our hearing, but we'd still be who we are. Our essences would remain.

Our brains contain our identities. All our memories, songs we know, personality traits, desires, loves and hates; they all reside in the mind. A stroke takes away more than physical abilities; it removes chunks of our very humanity. This complicates the recovery process. The awareness that a piece of my essence had died led to feelings of inadequacy.

Further, recovery from brain damage happens through us, the victims. No one can retrain our brains from the outside. Cancer is *treated* with chemotherapy or radiation. Diabetes is *treated* with insulin and diet restrictions. A stroke victim *recovers* through therapy and training. Brain damage cannot be treated by outside sources. Those of us who are recovering from strokes must treat ourselves. We get help and guidance from therapists, but we have to do the work. No one can repair our brains for us. We may take drugs to thin our blood, but that's only to prevent strokes from recurring. Drugs can't cure neuron damage. No treatment can regenerate

Jarvis Hooten

muscle control or speech cognition. No portion of the brain, not even a fragment the size of a baby aspirin, can be transplanted. Healing from a stroke is performed by the victim of the stroke. We, the possessors and masters of our minds, are the only ones who can rebuild them.

This is huge. It's hard to wrap our minds around restoring our minds. Our brains are the cores of our beings. Our minds control us, and we control our minds. This is why machines will never take over, contrary to popular science fiction themes. Centuries from now, we may develop computers with the speed and capacity of a human brain, although I have doubts about that, but no machine will ever have a will. No robot will be compelled by desire or a sense of purpose. The only intent a computer can have is intent that is programmed into it. Who does the programming? Humans. We tell computers to perform *our* wills. We humans determine our recoveries from stroke by the force of our wills. No machine and no other person can do it for us.

Computer geeks like to confuse Artificial Intelligence with Artificial Intent. Only living things have intent. Desire, hope, courage, commitment, conviction – all intentions derive from consciousness. Discipline is easy for a robot. It has no concept of fear or laziness or determination. A machine will persist at a task until it falls apart or until someone – some person – turns it off. This is what we like about machines. They'll work round the clock without complaint. Humans need motivation to work. We only do what we will ourselves to do. Every action we take, every task we perform, originates from a conscious decision.

You may be in the most difficult circumstance of your life. Emotions may be out of control, and you may not see any hope for the days and years ahead. It may be the hardest thing you've ever done, but you can will yourself to carry on. In time, hope and purpose will come back. If you've done anything worthwhile in your life, if anyone has reason to care whether or not you're around, you have purpose.

To bring my point into brutal perspective, if your life has been pure evil; if you have lived entirely by hurting and taking from others; if you're a despicable person like a character from a gangster movie, someone who has killed people and destroyed communities without remorse, then you deserve a disabling stroke, and you don't deserve to recover. The world is better off without you. What a horrible thing to say, right? Stay with me for a moment.

Now and then I come across stories of lifetime criminals, people who are truly evil to the core. Some rare individuals are so deeply flawed they destroy everyone who comes into contact with them. There are demons who get everything they have by hurting others. Be thankful such wretches are uncommon.

You may feel your life has lost its value, that you have nothing to hope for, no one to live for. Brain damage can take the mind into dark places. When despair takes over your thoughts, consider this: Somewhere, someone is glad you exist. Someone would be sad if you were gone. Incredibly, this may be someone you haven't met yet.

~ ~ ~ ~

Several times in this book I have referred to my Uncle

Jarvis Hooten

Lloyd, who had a stroke at age fifty and spent the rest of his life in a wheelchair. Here's the rest of his story:

Lloyd's massive stroke happened in 1988. His wife left him a few months later. He had left his first wife and six children to marry the woman who then left him after the stroke, so some thought there was righteous karma going on, but that's a family drama I won't go into.

Losing the use of his left leg and left arm, then losing his wife, put Lloyd into a depression for several years. He gave up on therapy altogether. It's likely he would have regained much of his abilities, had he not quit trying.

I didn't see much of my uncle in the early nineties. He lived in a suburb of Los Angeles, and I was enjoying the short-lived peak of my radio career in Nashville. It's difficult to appreciate how much he must have struggled during that time. Knowing what I know now, I wish I had reached out to him more.

In the late 1990s, a new technology began exploding all over the world. It was the dawn of the internet age, and it was a godsend to people like Lloyd. Suddenly, he had the world at his fingertips. He learned how to use a computer, navigate the web, and he became quite adept at one-handed typing. Having nothing else to do with his time, he discovered dozens of new options to pursue as a disabled person. He taught himself how to design web pages. That skill would benefit him a few years later.

In 2001, Lloyd's brother helped found a real estate agency in Albuquerque, New Mexico. The new agency needed a website to be part of the burgeoning internet phenomenon. "Hey, my brother knows how to do websites," Lloyd's brother proposed to the real estate agency, "How about we make him our webmaster?"

Millennials can't comprehend this now, but in 2001, web design was considered a sophisticated computer skill. Most people accessed the internet through dial-up connections. (For you young folks, that means over their telephone lines. Wait, do Millennials know what a telephone line is?) Lloyd was the first person I knew who had broadband. He struck a deal with the Albuquerque real estate agency to design and maintain the company's website for one percent of total commissions earned by the agents. Lloyd did all the design work from his small apartment in La Brea, California. He never had to leave home, and he worked on his own schedule – a dream job for anybody, but particularly for a disabled person.

For the first few years of the 2000s, Lloyd enjoyed a modest but satisfying income from his position as webmaster for a small real estate firm. Then came the boom. The agency grew substantially. By 2008, Lloyd's earnings shot up to over $75K per year. A disabled man, confined to a wheelchair and pushing seventy years old, was earning more than double the median income of the rest of the nation. I'm not sure how this affected his disability income. It probably didn't matter. With the amount he was earning, Lloyd didn't need disability.

I'm old enough to remember when there was no internet. So was my Uncle Lloyd. In 1988, the year he had his stroke, very few people owned personal computers. Hardly anyone had heard the word *Internet*, much less knew what it was. The World Wide Web didn't launch until August of 1991. Lloyd's life-changing job as webmaster was not possible until a decade after his stroke.

Brain damage can cause a person to think their life is over, that there is nothing to hope for or look forward to. You may not be able to see it now or know what it is. It may not exist yet, but something wonderful is waiting to be discovered.

Don't give up hope, don't lose faith. None of us knows what may lie ahead. A quality life after brain damage is more achievable now than at any other time in history. Possibilities improve every year.

~ ~ ~ ~

I hope you find hope. I encourage you to be courageous. I understand what you wish others understood. May the disaster of a brain injury benefit your life, as it has benefited my life, with the appreciation of what truly matters to you.

Overheard in the neuron break
lounge:

"Everyone expects us to do
things at the synapse of their
fingers."

"The brain stem is calling again?
The nerve of that guy!"

"I think everyone around here
knows something."
"Yeah? I know everyone around
here thinks something."

Made in the USA
Monee, IL
03 October 2022

15141182R00111